THE
STEAM THRASHING
TRADE

by

Michael Thexton, M.A.(Cantab)

Regency Press (London & New York) Ltd.
Chaucer House, Chaucer Business Park,
Kemsing, Sevenoaks, Kent TN15 6PW

ISBN 0 7212 0916 5

Printed and bound in Great Britain by
Buckland Press Ltd., Dover, Kent.

THE
STEAM THRASHING
TRADE

Front Cover:
Steam thrashing in Chile in February 1988. Ransomes, Sims & Jefferies portable engine number 40083 (1929), an 8 n.h.p. single cylinder, drives a Case thrashing machine near Catripulli, east of Pucón in southern Chile. The engine is being fired by Gaspar Muñoz, the owner of the set, who was carrying out contract thrashing for local farmers. Transparency by Ian Thomson, Chile.

Back Cover:
A timeless scene in February 1990 of steam thrashing in southern Chile in the vicinity of Misión de la Costa. Ransomes, Sims & Jefferies number 32084, a 4 n.h.p. single cylinder portable, drives a Chilean-built 'Morawitz' thrasher owned by Arsenio Antrillado. Transparency by Ian Thomson, Chile.

In this Hertfordshire scene, contractor John Patten thrashes barley at Buntingford in February 1936. The thrashing machine is driven by a Clayton and Shuttleworth traction engine, number 45235 of 1912, which was exhibited at the Doncaster Royal Show.

Contents

By the same Author

Steam Thrashing in the Cotswolds

Foreword

The Steam Thrashing Trade is an absorbing and scholarly book, especially to me, being brought up with steam thrashing – feeding the sheaves, driving the engine, and eventually owning. I also became a member of the National Traction Engine Owners and Users Association – earning their ire when leaving steam for tractors.

In 1937, when in Lincoln for a summer as an 'improver' at Foster's, I lived with the sadness of the falling trade of which Michael Thexton is more explicit. I never realised that Clayton and Shuttleworth – about 1908 – made more than thirty thrashing sets a week. It is sad that they have gone, but the name Shuttleworth is still known for historic aircraft, reminiscent of their World War I production of those mostly wooden machines.

Mention is also made of George Thurlow and Sons. I bought my Marshall tractors from them, in part-exchange for steam traction engines.

Readers will have difficulty in putting this book down – as indeed did I!

Esmond Kimbell
February 1997

Preface

During my research into steam thrashing, the idea arose of investigating key areas of the steam thrashing trade. The findings are contained in the following chapters, and by writing this book it is hoped to contribute to the picture of how the trade functioned.

Part One explores aspects of the export market, using the central theme of the Lincoln manufacturers. This approach continues in the early pages of Part Two before turning to 'Sales' and 'George Thurlow and Sons Limited'.

Part Three views the trade through the experiences of those who were part of it. The book concludes in Part Four by rounding-up and taking stock of the situation during and after the First World War.

Research for a book such as this is very much a co-operative effort, and to all those who assisted – both at home and abroad – I owe a debt of gratitude.

'Tallett Steps'   Michael Thexton, M.A.(Cantab)
Barnsley   January 1997
Cirencester
Gloucestershire

List of Illustrations

Acknowledgements

I wish to express my thanks to the following people and organisations who have assisted in several ways and given freely of their time in researching and preparing the information for this book. They are:

Mr. D. W. Astor, C.B.E., Mrs. A. Bates, Dr. Z. Bauer (Prague), Mr. R. Brooks, the late Mr. and Mrs. G. W. Cox, Mr. P. Farkas (Budapest), Mr. R. Griffin, Mrs. R. Gwynne-Jones, Mr. I. Jones, Mr. R. Last, the late Mr. H. D. Marshall, Mrs. M. H. Needs, Mr. D. Nourse, Mr. S. Philp, Mr. G. Poulton, Mr. J. A. Powell, Mr. R. Stanniforth, Mr. R. Pumfrey, Mr. J. Tester, the late Mrs. B. J. Thexton, Mr. R. Thexton, Mr. I. Thomson (Chile), Mrs. J. Timms.

Cambridgeshire Collection, Cambridgeshire Libraries: Mr. C. Jakes, Mr. M Petty; *Cambridge Evening News*: Mr. C. Tarrant; Cogges Manor Farm Museum, D.L.A., O.C.C.: Mrs. C. Mason; *Coventry Evening Telegraph*: Mr. M. Hepple; The Design Council: Mr. C. Ledsome; *The Engineer*: Mrs. C. Strachan, Mr. R. Northcott; *Engineering* magazine: Mr. P. Welch; The Hulton Getty Picture Collection: Mr. L. Oigo, Mrs. C. Theakstone; Hungarian Publishers and Booksellers Association, Budapest: Mr. P. Zentai; RÁBA Kispesti Öntöde-És Gépgyár KFT: Mr. Dénes István; HMSO: Mrs. P. Beckley; Local Studies Collection, Lincoln Central Library, Lincolnshire County Council, Education and Cultural Services Directorate: Mrs. S. H. Medd, Mrs. E. Nannestad; *Lincoln Chronicle*: Mr. M. Lyon; *Lincolnshire Life*: Mrs. J. Freeman, Mr. D. N. Robinson (former editor); *The Machinery Market*: Miss S. Wadham; Museum of Lincolnshire Life: Mr. A. Davies; National Maritime Museum: Mr. C. Gray; National Traction Engine Trust: Mr. R. West; The Oakwood Press: Mrs. J. Kennedy; Oxfordshire Museums Store, D.L.A., O.C.C.: Mr. P. Platt; Mr. W. Dickens; Oxfordshire Photographic Archives, D.L.A., O.C.C.: Mrs. N. La Vertue; Quiller Press Ltd; Road Locomotive Society: Mr. R. A. Harding, the late Mr. A. Duke; Royal Agricultural College Library: Miss T. Holloway, Mrs. S. Howie, Mrs. G. Young; The Royal Agricultural Society of England: Mrs. A. Sands; Suffolk Record Office: Mrs. R. Phillips, Mrs. A. West.

The Bodleian Library, University of Oxford: Mr. T. Dunnet; Mrs. S. Harris.

My thanks are also due to the following people who have provided research facilities and access to literature, records and documents:

Mr. J. M. Learmont and Mr. G. J. H. Rainey of Avdel plc; Dr. J. H. Brown and Mr. J. S. Creasey of the Rural History Centre, University of Reading; Mr. J. Thurlow and Mr. H. Armstrong of George Thurlow and Sons Limited.

Finally, my thanks to Mr. E. E. Kimbell and to Mr. R. E. Hooley – to Mr. Kimbell for writing the Foreword and for contributing: and to Mr. Hooley, Archivist at European Gas Turbines Limited, for reading the draft manuscript and assisting with research.

Many people have contributed photographs, and I wish to acknowledge their kindness in doing so. Owing to the passage of time it has on many occasions proved impossible to name the photographer and to give credit, and to these people I offer my apologies for any omissions, which are entirely unintended. Where known, the photographer of a scene has been acknowledged, or the source of the loan of the photograph stated, in the 'List of Illustrations'.

PART ONE

CHAPTER I

Aspects of Lincoln's trade with Hungary
and the rise of Hofherr Schrantz, 1852-1912

Within the U.K., probably the largest centre for the manufacture of complete thrashing sets was the cathedral city of Lincoln. That is not to overlook other centres and makers, but rather to emphasise Lincoln's unique status as the cradle of four companies producing portable engines, traction engines, and the associated thrashing machinery.

Clayton and Shuttleworth, Foster's, Robey's and Ruston Proctor were founded during the fifteen years between 1842 and 1857. Their broad thrust was into the export markets, and one of these was the significant if turbulent market of Hungary. The developing Hungarian grain lands attracted thrashing manufacturers from Austria, Germany, England and Hungary itself, whilst the principal centres of this trade were Vienna and Budapest, the leading cities of the Austro-Hungarian Empire.

Since Austria and Hungary enjoyed a Customs Union from 1867, Hungarian 'exports' from Vienna were exempt from 'import' duty in Hungary and could therefore effectively compete on the Hungarian home market. In practice, two of the largest thrashing manufacturers had factories in both Vienna and Budapest, the companies concerned being Clayton and Shuttleworth and Hofherr Schrantz.

Lincoln's trade with Hungary began in 1852 when Clayton and Shuttleworth supplied the first steam thrashing set to be used in the country. Other builders developed business and during 1862 more than two hundred thrashing sets were at work.[1]

However, three of the Lincoln companies established manufacturing subsidiaries in either Budapest or Vienna between 1857 and 1872 – Foster's and Robey's in Budapest, Clayton and Shuttleworth in Vienna. The apparent reasons for this were the competitive advantages deriving from the elimination of import duties, reduced freightage and lower manufacturing costs – bearing in mind that wages were around 15% lower than in England.[2] There are also grounds for considering that the Hungarian Government may have actively encouraged these moves since it is known that Marshall's were invited to establish a factory in 1885.[3]

The first stage in exporting – loading ship – in this instance at Southampton, where Fowler road locomotives are being hoisted aboard the S.S. Denton Grange in 1899.

The case for the subsidiaries became more compelling in 1882. Import duties were raised to 8 to 10% for a portable and were subsequently increased to 20 to 23% by 1904.[4]

William Foster's involvement began in Budapest in 1860 when he set up a branch works and repair facility for portable engines and thrashing machines. Later, he diversified and established a ship building yard on the River Danube where several torpedo boats were constructed in 1873.

By 1885-86, a link had been forged with the agricultural machinery manufacturers W. N. Nicholson and Sons of Newark, and the Foster Budapest factory traded under the name of 'Nicholson and Company'.[5]

The Hungarian market also attracted Robey's, who opened a small factory in Budapest in 1872. Corn grinding mills were the initial products, but portable engines and thrashing machines followed during the 1880s.[6]

Contrary to the trend, it appears that Ruston Proctor's policy was one of persevering with exports: the Author has been unable to trace a Hungarian manufacturing capability. The gist of the evidence which the then managing director gave to the Tariff Commission in 1904 was that the only way in which his company could continue to do business in Austria-Hungary was by absorbing the duty. In effect, the duty was paid by the manufacturer, not by the consumer. Profit margins were therefore adversely affected in this highly competitive market.[7]

Clayton and Shuttleworth's Landstrasse Works at Vienna, 1897.

Undoubtedly the largest subsidiary was the Clayton and Shuttleworth Landstrasse Works which opened in Vienna in 1857. Enjoying duty-free access to the Hungarian market, a wide range of agricultural machinery was produced, ranging from ploughs and grinding mills to portable engines and thrashing machines. By 1883, over two hundred were employed, rising to twelve hundred in 1907.

This was overseas business on a grand scale, and a little colour to the facts can be gleaned from the experiences of Alfred Shuttleworth's valet, the late Mr. J. H. Everett. In his obituary it was recorded that: '. . . On 22 occasions he went with Mr. Alfred Shuttleworth on business to Austria, and at which time it was nearly always attended by a visit to the Imperial Palace at Vienna, as well as many other notable residences of the country . . . '.[8]

The Lincoln subsidiaries – and for that matter, the Lincoln parent companies – faced tough competition from the growing ranks of native manufacturers. The 1880s marked the rise of the Hungarian steam thrashing industry and in particular Hofherr Schrantz and the agricultural engineering activities of the Hungarian Royal States Railways Factories (M.A.V.A.G.).

Part of the portable engine erecting shop at the Hungarian Royal States Railways Factories, Budapest, circa 1908.

The combination known as the Hungarian Royal States Railway Factories began making portable engines and thrashing machines at their Budapest works in 1877. By 1886, the works was being enlarged to produce a projected annual output of 250 sets. These thrashing sets were being sold ' . . . at prices with which no English manufacturers are able to compete, and at terms of payment divided into instalments over several years . . . ' reported the British Consul-General for Hungary in 1886.[9]

By 1908, annual output had doubled to 500 sets, thrashing sets were being exported to Russia, and a range of traction engines and steam rollers were under construction.[10] There is evidence to support the view that English thrashing manufacturers regarded the Hungarian Royal States Railways Factories as a major competing force in Hungary.[11]

In the private sector, Hofherr Schrantz were one of a number of companies to commence the manufacture of steam thrashing sets. Here the Author wishes to acknowledge Dénes István, the managing director of Hofherr Schrantz's successors, for permission to draw from the company's official history.[12]

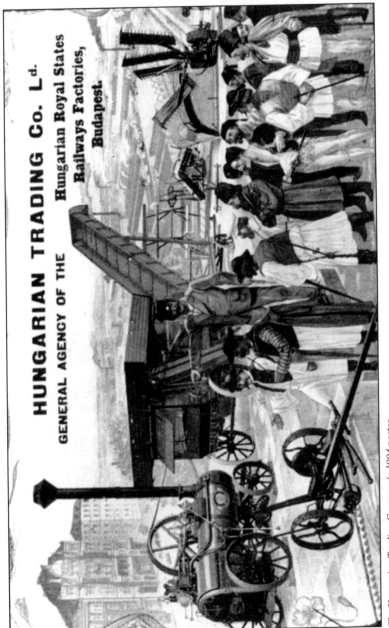

The Hungarian Trading Company's 1904 poster.

Mátyás Hofherr, the founder of Hofherr Schrantz, was the son of a smallholder and was born in Germany in 1829. He began his career as a locksmith's apprentice. When he 'came out of his time', he visited France, England and Switzerland before settling in Vienna in the 1850s. This was where Hofherr familiarised himself with agricultural machinery and steam power, becoming works manager of a company of Hungarian origin to whom he introduced his own designs.

Mátyás Hofherr, founder of Hofherr Schrantz.

Before joining Clayton and Shuttleworth's Vienna factory in 1862, Hofherr spent a number of years at Odessa. At Clayton's he became manager of the rapidly expanding Vienna factory which was producing agricultural machinery and steam thrashing sets. Seven years later, at the age of forty and with a number of patents to his name, Hofherr left Clayton and Shuttleworth to establish his own company in Vienna under the name of 'Hofherr and Company'.

Harvesters based on the 'Samuelson' system were his initial products, but they incorporated improvements designed by Hofherr. Clayton and Shuttleworth sold and promoted Hofherr harvesters.

In 1881, Janos Schrantz, who carried out product development at Hofherr's, became a partner and the 'Hofherr Schrantz Farm Machine Works and Iron Foundry' was born. Shortly afterwards, the Vienna factory was enlarged and modernised and started making portable engines and thrashing machines which were distributed throughout Hungary and to branches in Austria, Russia and Roumania.

Inescapably, these products and outlets encroached on Clayton and Shuttleworth's trade and as competition intensified the relationship cooled.

During the next phase, Clayton and Shuttleworth and Hofherr Schrantz established factories in Budapest between 1885 and 1891, culminating in Hofherr Schrantz's large new factory at Kispest in eastern Budapest in 1900. Just two years earlier, Hofherr Schrantz had dispatched their ten-thousandth thrasher.

Events now took a strange turn. During 1911-12, Hofherr Schrantz decided to expand their Vienna operation but they were hemmed-in: establishing a new factory and transferring the old would have proved costly. Meanwhile Clayton's works – which had moved to Floridsdorf in 1905 – was in a loss-making situation. This was the background to Clayton's surprising proposal to sell to Hofherr Schrantz the Floridsdorf factory together with the Hungarian, Bulgarian and Roumanian concerns. The sale was approved by the shareholders of the Lincoln parent company in October 1911.

Terms were agreed and the take-over was effective from the 1st of January, 1912. Hofherr Schrantz incorporated the Clayton and Shuttleworth name in the title of the new company which was known as 'Hofherr-Schrantz-Clayton-Shuttleworth' – or H.S.C.S. for short. H.S.C.S. was re-named the 'Red Star Tractor Factory' in March 1948. Now, after the fall of the communist regime, the company is called the 'Foundry and Machine Factory of Kispest'.

Amongst the products of Hofherr Schrantz and H.S.C.S. were direct-traction ploughing engines, single-engine ploughing sets, and double-engine cable ploughing sets. This was in addition to portable engines, traction engines, thrashing machines and agricultural machinery.

The repercussions of Clayton and Shuttleworth's disposals and their trade in central and eastern Europe rumbled on long after 1912. Ultimately the foreign debts and loss of investments in Austria-Hungary, Russia, Roumania and Bulgaria amounted to £520,000 when written-off by Clayton and Shuttleworth in 1919.[13] This burden proved to be a contributory factor to the firm's approaching demise.

By 1912, therefore, the largest of the Lincoln subsidiaries had been absorbed by a Hungarian concern. This leaves Foster's and Nicholson's, who had already sold their interests to a Budapest syndicate in 1887, and Robey's whose sales in Hungary showed a 98% decrease between 1873 and 1903. In fact, as Robey's Frederick Andrew stated to the Tariff Commission, ' . . . the trade is nearly wiped out'.[14]

Such were some of the experiences of the Lincoln firms in their bid to exploit the Hungarian market from within. Starting from a position of unrivalled technology, the mushrooming of second-generation competition eventually led to their position becoming untenable. Here we see the growth of the native industry, encouraged by government assistance including free transport to the frontiers for cross-border trade and bounties for export performance.[15]

It is reasonably certain that exporting through the normal channels offered the only avenue for continuing the Hungarian trade. That this was likely to be severely restricted was revealed by J. E. Ransome's evidence to the Tariff Commission circa 1904: ' . . . There were, roughly speaking, 800 sets of steam thrashing machines exported annually from this country to Austria-Hungary some 20 years ago, and now not above 10% of that number . . . '.[16] J. E. Ransome, it should be added, was the chairman of Ransomes, Sims and Jefferies Limited of Ipswich.

In the final analysis, the combination of the highly-protected market and the competitive home industry led to the Lincoln builders concentrating their efforts elsewhere – such as the distant Argentine – to develop the high-volume trade which they were seeking and which could be conducted under more favourable trading conditions.

An illustration of a Hofherr Schrantz bevel-geared traction engine built at Budapest in 1902.

CHAPTER II

Developments in the export trade

The export trade flourished whilst agricultural depression blighted home sales through the late nineteenth and early twentieth century.[1] During the period 1882 to 1907, for which figures are available, Germany, Russia and the Argentine were the leading countries for U.K. exports of 'Agricultural Steam Engines'.[2]

Not only portable engines and thrashing machines were being exported: the Lincoln firms developed a complementary line in traction engines, an addition to the range of steam thrashing machinery already being distributed through agents and branches. To keep matters in perspective it is only fair to add that abroad, in the established markets of the grain producers, the simple, inexpensive portable, burning a variety of locally-available fuels, remained the primary source of power throughout the age of steam. At Foster's, for instance, about ten portable sets were being sold for each traction set during the halcyon years between 1905 and 1910.[3]

Nonetheless, the impact of the traction engine was significant and the Lincoln builders produced a range of specialist tractions to suit the needs of agriculturalists working under very different conditions of climate, terrain and fuel supply. 'Standard' and 'modified' versions were exported, but the twin pressures of price and competition provided the spur for the sales and drawing offices to innovate and respond to local conditions where a worthwhile demand was envisaged.

Although Britain possessed the technological edge in the earlier days, as time went on the export market became increasingly competitive. Foreign manufacturers sprang up, protected in many instances by import tariffs, and the North American builders became a force to be reckoned with. Against this scenario a number of the English builders were fighting for their slice of the business. Consequently the specialist engines we are talking about were very much 'built to a price', and here one should bear in mind that the final selling price needed to be competitive after freightage costs, import charges and agent's commission had been accounted for.

In drawing up these new designs the opportunity was taken to produce machines which were more economical in material and construction costs. As

Thrashing with a portable engine at Rectory Farm, Cherryhinton, Cambridgeshire. The ubiquitous portable and thrashing machine was the bedrock of the export drive into the world's grain lands.

Clayton's pointed out in one of their catalogues, weight-reduction worked to everyone's advantage by reducing freightage costs and import charges, particularly where the latter were calculated on the weight of machinery supplied.

As far as thrashing was concerned, production of specialist traction engines ranged from the 'Light-types' and 'Self-propelling engines' to larger and more powerful machines which were capable of both thrashing and direct-traction ploughing. A parallel but separate development was the laying-down of specific types whose primary purpose was heavy, continuous ploughing but with the flexibility of use in the thrashing role by the addition of governors.

The 'Light-types' made a direct appeal to the farmer abroad who wanted to progress from a portable and required little more than the ability to haul and drive the smaller sizes of thrashing machine and to carry out light farm work – in other words, the first step onto the ladder for the would-be traction engine owner. The next step was to the larger and more powerful machines which could be set at direct-ploughing and the largest thrashing machines. The reasoning behind producing a traction engine which could also double-up as a ploughing engine hardly calls for elaboration: the advantages for the farmer are self-evident. Suffice to say that in these most versatile machines the agriculturalist abroad at long last had the nearest approach to a truly 'farmers engine', and an engine, moreover, which could be used all the year round.

From these strands of development the arrangement of the various types could be synthesised into coal, wood or straw-burning; friction clutch or conventional drive; single or compound. The usual hallmarks of most types were lighter weight for a given power and improved travelling across country using wider wheels and deep strakes. Local conditions played a part – for example, in cold climates such as the Baltic States, feedwater tanks under the boiler barrel and steam-warming coils were offered.

Commercial judgement can be fogged by detail so we must not overlook the fact that business development for the large exporter of steam thrashing machinery was based on offering a wide range of portables, traction engines and thrashing machinery targeted at the farming community as a whole – not just the large estate-owners. For the same overheads and sales effort, a number of products could be sold and better shipping rates secured.

The nature of the thrashing operation in a major grain-growing country such as Argentina was on a much larger scale than on the home market. To pursue the example of Argentina, time was crucial where much of the grain was exported, for the stages of harvesting, thrashing and consigning to the ports had to be

Robey tandem-compound straw-burning traction engine at the works. Note spark-catcher adjusting rod at the front of the chimney, deep strakes and ashpan to hold water to minimise the fire risk.

carried out rapidly to avoid deterioration of the stock and 'shelling-out' of the standing grain in the field. Furthermore, in Argentina the harvest was thrashed in the short period – by British standards – of three months, January to March, and the season's work for a thrashing machine was reckoned at about forty-five days.[4]

The need therefore arose for a thrashing machine with a higher output than was customary on the home market. Larger thrashing machines were introduced, incorporating 'American' features such as the 'automatic elevator band-cutter feeder' and 'wind' or pneumatic straw stackers.[5] These labour-saving improvements were particularly effective in the Argentine where contemporary observers stressed both the scarcity of trained farm hands and the high wages commanded during harvest time.[6]

Sales promotion in Argentina for maker and agent – the Clayton and Shuttleworth/Drysdale show card, 1903.

The first thrashing machine was imported into Argentina in 1858. By the time of the 1909 harvest, 5,600 thrashers were in operation, usually portable or traction-powered, and of this total 736 were American, 12 German, and 4,864 British. Over 1,900 were manufactured by Clayton and Shuttleworth alone, the largest single supplier. Thrashing machines were being imported at the average rate of 1,000 per year between 1907 and 1911, the most popular drum width being the five foot. Other sizes supplied were the 3'6", 4'0", 4'6" and 5'6".[7]

Hot work for the fireman tending a Clayton and Shuttleworth tandem-compound straw-burner. Note the fire extinguishing hose curling down towards the straw rack. This all-Clayton rig was photographed in Argentina in 1909.

Towards the end of thrashing, the automatic feeder on the thrasher is angled downwards to meet the remains of the stack. The tandem-compound straw-burning traction engine, and thrashing machine, were built by Clayton and Shuttleworth. This photograph, which was taken in 1909, conveys an impression of the scale and atmosphere of steam thrashing in Argentina.

Canada and Australia pointed the way to the future with the introduction of the 'Stripper-harvester' where cutting, thrashing and bagging occurred in one process on a horse and latterly tractor-hauled machine: as many as 586 were at work during the 1909 season.[8]

As we have said, time was at a premium when large crops had to be thrashed and another time-saving – if not cost-saving feature – which was incorporated in many export traction engines was the 'friction clutch'. This enabled the driver to 'inch' his engine whilst actually driving the thrashing machine, and was particularly valuable in hot climates where longer belts were used to minimise the fire risk by positioning the engine as far away from the thrashing machine as was practicable. As the sun rose to its intensity the belt stretched and easing back with the friction clutch avoided innumerable delays through having to stop, put the engine in and out of gear and then run the machine up to speed.

One of the most significant developments which went hand-in-hand with thrashing was the introduction of straw-burning portables and traction engines. Straw was produced in large quantities whilst thrashing and in areas such as the Argentinian pampas there was little call for animal feed or bedding and the straw was virtually without value. However, the prevailing climate had to be dry enough to permit the crop to be thrashed in the field immediately after reaping so that the engine could be fired with dry straw. This was one of the points made by Dan Pidgeon in a contribution to the *Journal of the Royal Agricultural Society of England* in 1892. He went on to comment on the economics of straw burning, to the effect that: '. . . the calorific value of straw is as 1 to 3½ compared with coal, or, taking the relative local values of coal and straw into consideration, the use of the former would cost 3½ times more than the latter in countries like Russia or Hungary. In England, on the other hand, coal is the cheaper fuel by 5 to 1, partly because of its own low price, and partly because of the high price of straw. . .'.[9]

One can imagine that thrashing with a straw-burning traction engine in hot, dry climates was like working in a veritable tinderbox. Elaborate precautions were taken to prevent the outbreak of fires from sparks, ashes and blowbacks. Engines were fitted with an independent 'general service' steam pump which drew water from the engine tank or water wagon and discharged through the fire extinguishing hose. Water filled ashpans and adjustable cone-wire spark catchers represented further measures to curb the ever-present fire hazard.

On a straw-burning traction engine, the crew consisted of a driver and a fireman who forked loose straw onto the firedoor mouthpiece and through the self-closing flap. When steaming across the pampas, the continuous job of firing-up 'on the move' was demanding, if not hazardous, and the fireman worked along an improvised platform stretching from the wooden rack on the back of the engine to the straw wagon. Coupled to this perhaps a living van which in turn trailed the thrashing machine or maize sheller, pictorial evidence suggesting that the water wagon was often hauled by a team of horses.

By adopting straw-burning designs, the engine builders scored a significant marketing success by providing remote farmers with a mobile power unit using locally-available fuel. Hand firing was preferable to mechanical feeding on traction engine work, and straw-burning grates could be adapted to burn wood or coal by substituting the makers' fittings.

Thousands of traction engines, portables and thrashing machines were imported into Argentina to thrash the cereal crops which in addition to home consumption were vital to the country's export drive and balance of payments. The removal of the Republic's 10% customs surtax in 1904 and 1905 encouraged thrashing machinery imports:[10] even so, British sales began to wane in the face of strong North American competition and by 1909 to 1910 the latter was edging up to 15% of all thrashing machine imports, with Lanz of Germany establishing a foothold in the market.[11]

Here one cannot but invite comparison between the Argentine Republic's removal of duty, and the Hungarian government's application of duty – two steam thrashing markets in which the maker encountered totally different trading conditions. In the Argentine, there was little in the way of a native steam thrashing industry, and imports were encouraged to process the important export commodity of grain: in Hungary, on the other hand, this need was largely met by the expanding and protected home industry.

To conclude our review, an extract will be included from the writings of Sir William Tritton, managing director of Foster's between 1906 and 1941. His name has always been associated with the invention of the Tank: perhaps less well-known was his contribution to steam thrashing. He was well-acquainted with the practical problems facing users of steam thrashing machinery and it is recorded that he travelled extensively to study the needs and to develop products for the Argentinian, Russian, Bulgarian and Roumanian markets.

Sir William's 1934 assessment is particularly relevant because it sheds light on the dimensions of the trade at its peak – which Sir William dates precisely as '. . . the period 1906 to 1912'.

He stated that '. . . Probably about 7,000 sets per annum represented the high water mark of this industry. This includes Maize Shellers and Huskers which, together with the motive power – either a steam portable or traction engine – represented a turnover of about £2,300,000 per annum. Of this the home trade did not account for more than 100 sets per year, and the value per set being a little higher (due to a preponderance of traction engines in lieu of portable engines) represented a home trade of about £55,000, leaving about 2¼ millions of exports . . .'.[12]

These factual statements throw into stark relief the relative proportions of home market and export sales at the 'high point' of the steam thrashing era. The figures re-emphasise the global nature of the trade and the comparatively small requirement of the U.K. running at 1.4% of total output between 1906 and 1912. How may this be explained? The intrusion of foreign machinery imports of

A single cylinder straw-burning Clayton moves on to the next job with tender-wagon, living van and Clayton maize sheller in tow. Photographed in Argentina in 1908.

An 'Advance' American traction engine, tandem compound, driving a Clayton maize sheller fitted with feed elevator and pneumatic stacker. The engine is being fired with maize cobs and this scene was photographed in Argentina.

steam thrashing equipment onto the home market may be discounted at this period, and perhaps instead one should turn to extremely competitive foreign grain imports and the adverse effect on home grain production. Against a declining market there was little incentive for widespread renewals, and saturation point may well have been reached as demand settled down to around a hundred sets per year.

PART TWO

CHAPTER III

Company matters and the
human side of business

The U.K. steam thrashing industry comprised an array of firms ranging from the small country engineering works to major industrial concerns. Production was diverse: some firms built complete thrashing sets, whilst offering engines and thrashing machines separately; others built either the engine or the machinery, relying on 'buying-in' to make up the complete set.

The 'backbone' of the industry – in the sense of large-scale manufacture of 'complete' sets – consisted, according to Sir William Tritton, of the Lincoln companies which have already been mentioned, and the following major concerns:

Richard Garrett & Sons Ltd., Leiston, Suffolk.
Richard Hornsby & Sons Ltd., Grantham, Lincolnshire.
Marshall, Sons & Co., Ltd., Gainsborough, Lincolnshire.
Ransomes, Sims & Jefferies Ltd., Ipswich, Suffolk.[1]

Viewed regionally, therefore, large-scale steam thrashing machinery manufacture was essentially an Eastern England enterprise, one of the principal agricultural areas in which crop production predominated.

Taking the long view, it should be remembered that the production of steam thrashing machinery usually represented a stage in the maker's development. Some sooner, some later, these firms began to develop a range of products which supplemented and then overshadowed their original steam thrashing business.

The Lincoln companies played a large part in that business. Between 1897 and 1904, just before the 'peak' years, around 5,500 were employed at the four firms. There were 1,800 at Clayton and Shuttleworth (1897), 400 at Foster's (1900), 1,500 at Robey's (1904), and 1,955 at Ruston Proctor (1896). These figures rose dramatically during the First World War, but in any event staff engaged on other products would have to be deducted in order to arrive at a precise assessment. However, the figures serve to give an indication of relative size.

An 1877 photograph of Robey's 'Globe Works' and the Canwick Road floods.

Before the First World War, the prosperity of Lincoln was to an extent dependent upon the fortunes of the factories in which the state of the steam thrashing trade played a large part. Vulnerable to the natural conditions affecting harvests the world over, the steam thrashing trade was hostage to drought, pestilence and the vagaries of the weather, which in turn affected the industry itself. Indeed, it was said that nowhere were the harvest reports read more anxiously than in Lincoln, where a good or bad harvest had a corresponding effect upon orders – not only for the principal factories, but also for the ancillary companies producing items such as forgings, corn-screens, waterproof covers and belting.

Good years or bad, today few can recall the atmosphere of pre-First World War Lincoln where so many were employed in the thrashing machine and engine factories. Down at 'Stamp End', a glimpse of Nathaniel Clayton shines through the following anecdotes which were penned in *The Lincolnshire Chronicle* by a former employee of Clayton and Shuttleworth in January 1945. Identifying himself as 'W. M.', and writing about the period before 1890, he recalled the time when '. . . a large Russian order for engines was in progress'. Apparently, '. . . two youths had to work on Saturday afternoons in the boiler shop making chimneys. Mr. Clayton regularly visited the "Chimney Corner", as that part of the shop was called, and after inspecting their work presented each with a threepenny-piece and warned them in his gruff way "not to spend it recklessly in the market at night" . . .'.

Then there was the small boy, '. . . who, one day, seeing the master coming down the street clad in his usual grey suit with bowler to match, plucked up courage to address him . . . "If you please, Mr. Clayton, will you let my dad make me an engine?" "Who is your dad, my little man?" the chief enquired sympathetically. The boy told him, and was informed that "He'd see to it". The little fellow got a skeleton locomotive on which he rode many times down the hilly streets near his home. These incidents show the close relationship between master and man that existed in those old days . . . '.

In similar vein, 'W. M.' emphasised that '. . . before the limited company days (1901) the works seemed more of a family affair, father, son and grandson in some cases being employed there at the same time . . .'. Moreover, and perhaps significantly, '. . . the heads knew every workman by name . . .'. Those were the days in which the foremen – '. . . those collar and tie gents . . .' – were 'granted the use of a horse to carry them in their business travels from shop to shop, and each was expected to wear a top-hat . . .'.[2]

These sketches go a little way towards shedding light on aspects of the prevalent industrial culture, a culture which often prized stability and length of service. Clayton's field engineer, David Richardson, who served with the company for sixty-three years (1857 to 1920), may perhaps be regarded as

The arch erected in Lincoln High Street on the occasion of King Edward 7th's visit to the Royal Show in 1907.

the exception rather than the rule: but the completion of fifty years with the same employer was by no means uncommon.[3]

One Lincoln maker struck a fifty-year service medal when the company itself reached this age. Both the recognition of long service and the opportunity to foster 'esprit de corps' formed part of the gold medal presentation at Ruston Proctor. It is suggested that the ceremony may well have been viewed with a certain amount of trepidation by the participants, for in those days the entire workforce was mustered and the recipient joined the directors on the dais where he was invited by the chairman to recount his experiences. Significantly, the medal portrayed the importance of the steam thrashing trade – on the face was a portable engine and thrashing machine (see below). It remains to say that the medal was accompanied with a pension and an easy chair.[4]

Around 1908, Clayton's manufactured 30 to 32 thrashing sets per week.[5] Impressive figures as they were, the export trade continued to become

A photograph of the gold medal for 50 years' service – first awarded by Ruston Proctor in July 1906.

increasingly competitive in the face of foreign manufacturers and trade tariffs. Put simply, business was increasing, but at a lower rate of profit. Companies were looking for ways to increase their efficiency.

Analysing and prescribing remedies proved to be a fruitful topic for British engineers and Clayton and Shuttleworth were no exception. One of the key areas for development was the improvement of technical education and training. When Clayton's appointed the American-born Harry Orcutt (1861-1942) as their managing director in 1904, they were recruiting an eminent authority on engineering methods and management with a knowledge of both the American and German systems. Before moving to Clayton's, Harry Orcutt – who at one time worked for Pratt and Whitney – became a consulting engineer with Ludwig, Loewe in Berlin.[6]

It may be safely assumed that Harry Orcutt's hand can be seen in the drafting of Clayton and Shuttleworth's new apprenticeship system of 1907. This enshrined his philosophy that '. . . manufacturers must establish systems of apprenticeship which include workshop experience under educational guidance . . .'[7] Fundamental as this may seem to us today, it was by no means the widespread practice at the time. Recognition of the pioneering nature of this scheme can be seen in its adoption as the first of a series of case studies on the 'Training of engineering apprentices' in the columns of *The Engineer* in 1908.

Bucking the trend, Clayton's abolished 'Premium' apprenticeships outright, they removed the fourteen-year-old age of entry, and opened the field to suitably educated fifteen to twenty-one-year-olds. Another radical departure was the shortening of apprenticeships from seven years to five to six years for entry at fifteen, and to three years in all trades for those aged eighteen to twenty-one.

Appreciation of the sometimes haphazard instruction gleaned under day-to-day production pressures was seen in the appointment of a 'superintendent', a 'father-figure' who was responsible for the general welfare and instruction of all apprentices. Perhaps the most significant innovation was the introduction of classes in which the principles and practices of the trade engineering processes were taught. As far as possible these classes paralleled the production work in the factory departments and were taught during the normal working routine. Unlike some schemes of the day, no financial loss was incurred whilst absent from the 'bread-and-butter' production work.

Whatever the motives, such an enlightened approach represented a milestone in the application of factory training by one of the steam thrashing industry's leading employers. This original and in some respects revolutionary scheme sheds light on Clayton's reactions to increasing competitiveness during the early 1900s.[8]

The new apprenticeship scheme materially assisted recruitment in so

The Portable Engine Erecting Shop at Ruston Proctor.

far as it assured parents of a first-rate training for their sons. From another aspect, it reflected just one of the many links between the industry and the city. Apart from their role as employers, there were many facets to the involvement of the Lincoln management, both in the community at large and in public life. To quote one example, in response to the Lincoln typhoid epidemic of 1905, both Alfred Shuttleworth and Colonel Ruston organised and personally paid for over fifty nurses and doctors in addition to playing a significant part in the relief operation.[9]

At a national level, officials rubbed shoulders at the Agricultural Engineers Association and the National Traction Engine Owners and Users Association, perhaps to meet again at the premier events of the year, the Smithfield Show and the Royal Show. In pursuit of both the export trade and the home trade, the A.E.A. (1877), and the N.T.E.O. & U.A. (1893), proved to be effective pressure groups. Overlapping memberships facilitated the exchange of views and the formation of a united front when mutual interests were threatened.

News of associations' negotiations filtered through to the trade at large via *The Implement and Machinery Review*. The influence exerted by the latter via their informative editorials played a valuable part in the opinion-forming process. In reality, all in the trade benefited – whether members or not – from the activities of the national organisations.

The bonds between manufacturers, agents and users were extensive, and with the 'editorial arm' – *The Implement and Machinery Review* – formed the 'heart' of the steam thrashing trade.

Apprentices studying at Clayton and Shuttleworth, circa 1908.

Foster's traction engine erecting shop at the Wellington Foundry, Lincoln.

CHAPTER IV

Sales

Moving on to the selling of steam thrashing sets, one should not over-look the influence of The Royal Agricultural Society of England in promoting the use of thrashing machinery through their shows, show trials and *The Journal*. By holding their annual shows at different locations each year, all that was latest was made more accessible to farmers in an age when rural communications were poor. The makers and their market were brought together, machinery could be seen at work and compared, and trials and awards with the attendant prestige provided an incentive to develop.

To give an idea of the scope of the Royal Shows in the earlier days, 112 portables and 55 thrashing machines were displayed at the Chester Royal Show in 1858.[1] Perhaps more typical of the later years was the representation at the Gloucester event held in 1909. Of the nine companies exhibiting steam thrashing machinery, the number of entries varied from two to ten per maker. Prices ranged between £485 and £520 for a seven nominal horsepower single cylinder agricultural engine, and from £150 to £171 for a standard 54" thrashing machine.[2]

A number of companies had London offices and showrooms. In an advertisement in the R.A.S.E. *Journal* in 1855, Clayton and Shuttleworth publicised that their portable steam engine and thrashing machines '. . . may be seen at work at their London establishment, 6 Fitzroy Terrace, New Road, every Monday, between the hours of 10 in the morning and 4 in the afternoon, and any other day by giving a few hours' notice. . .'[3]

But what about the day-to-day business of selling portables, thrashing machines and traction engines onto the home market? Manufacturers' representatives visited farmers, contractors, and agents and in addition to dispensing literature might well invite intending purchasers for a visit to the factory. Whether out on the thrashing round or at agricultural shows, sociable chat, snippets of news and suggestions from a personable salesman provided a little relief and encouraged continuity. Business was business, and contact of a personal nature was one of the best ways of promoting it.

Another avenue of selling was via the services of an agent – perhaps engineers, repairers or dealers – thus indirectly giving the manufacturer access to

Part of Ruston Proctor's display at the 1907 Royal Show at Lincoln.

the agent's circle of customers in a locality, often via the agent's own representatives. However, agents had to be carefully regulated with defined territories to avoid a chaotic situation developing. At one end of the spectrum was a small concern, such as the Aveling agent at Northleach, W. M. Teall; at the other end of the spectrum there were agents with country-wide connections such as George Thurlow and Sons Limited, to whom we will turn in the next chapter.

The trade between manufacturers and agents worked both ways. Through their specialist knowledge of the second-hand market, agents relieved manufacturers of the time-consuming business of finding buyers for used engines and machinery taken in part-exchange, a peripheral trade in which they hardly wished to become involved. The late Henry Marshall told the Author that the greater part of Marshall's used engines were sold to George Thurlow for disposal, and it is recorded in the Clayton sales records that another East Anglian agent, James Graven and Sons of Ely, provided a similar facility for Clayton and Shuttleworth. Graven's sales encompassed not only the U.K., but extended overseas to Canada.

Seemingly no stone was left unturned in the quest for sales. At least one manufacturer adopted the tactic of following up advertisements in the trade press by would-be buyers. When Caleb Lainchbury of Kingham advertised in *Machinery Market* for a second-hand traction engine in 1915, he evoked the response from Marshall's which is reproduced on page 52. Presumably there was someone at Marshall's charged with the task of scouring the columns, prompting the speculative reply from Herbert Marshall in 1915.

Whether a sale resulted is not known: but it may be of interest to add that George Keightley, mentioned in Herbert Marshall's letter, was a key member of Marshall's sales staff.

George Keightley came to Marshall's from the Gainsborough Steam Packet Company, and his route into sales was via the estimating and correspondence departments of which he was initially appointed the manager in 1868. Subsequently he became well known in the steam thrashing trade as Marshall's Midland Counties representative and latterly as their senior representative covering the Midlands and South-West England. All in all, he worked for Marshall's for fifty years until his death in harness in 1918.[4]

Evidently sales ability ran in the family, for his son Walter joined the company in 1887 and followed a rather similar career which was broadened with four years as Clayton and Shuttleworth's representative between 1900 and 1914, and secondment to the Food Production Department allocating thrashing sets during the First World War. After continuing with Marshall's in a senior sales capacity, he was appointed the manager of the London office in 1928, from where he took up a directorship with T. Baker and Sons (Compton) Limited some two years prior to his death in October 1933.[5]

Selling onto the home market was very different from the somewhat tortuous process of selling thrashing tackle many thousands of miles away overseas. If

UNDER GOVERNMENT CONTROL,

MARSHALL, SONS & Co. Ltd.

TELEGRAMS FOR WORKS: "MARSHALLS GAINSBOROUGH"
TELEPHONE: No. 40 GAINSBOROUGH (2 LINES)

BRITANNIA IRONWORKS

TELEGRAMS FOR LONDON OFFICE: "ENGINE
SMITH
LONDON"
TELEPHONE: No. 648 HOLBORN, LONDON

GAINSBOROUGH, ENGLAND

CODES
OUR OWN. A. B. C. (4TH. & 5TH. EDITIONS). A I (1888 EDITION)
ENGINEERING.   LIEBERS.   WESTERN UNION

20th. August 1915
REFERENCES

OURS W.F.B. PD.   YOURS

Messrs. C. Lainchbury & Son.

Kingham, Oxon.

Dear Sirs,

Referring to your advertisement in the current issue of "Machinery Market", we have nothing suitable second-hand which we can offer you, but we have in stock ready for prompt delivery a 6 N.H.P. Single Cylinder Traction Engine of our latest standard type, as illustrated and described on pages 9 to 13 of the accompanying catalogue No871.

If you can entertain a quotation for this engine, we shall be pleased to send you a detailed specification and estimate; or we could arrange for our Midland Counties Representative - Mr. George Keightley - to visit your place and talk over the matter with your goodselves.

We shall be glad to hear from you on this subject.

Yours faithfully

MARSHALL, SONS & COMPANY, LIMITED

Sales letter from Herbert Marshall to Caleb Lainchbury and Son.

the business warranted it, then a branch and possibly a repair facility might be set up: alternatively, agents would be sought, varying in stature from concerns with international connections to the local company on the spot. Local agents would need to be carefully vetted, and discreet enquiries would be made as J. R. Marshall discovered during his research into the Clayton and Shuttleworth export agreements: '. . . Before agents could be appointed it was necessary to make some enquiries as to their character and business standing. This must often have been a somewhat delicate matter, and it is interesting to see that a fair amount of co-operation existed between English firms, who though competitors for business had apparently a common interest in protecting each other from losses from sharp practitioners. The reports from foreign sources are however most amusing. One potential agent is said "to have lately married 2,000 florins and built a substantial house, and has good prospects". A member of a partnership is said "to have left his last situation after deficiencies which he has declined to explain". His partner's character was however thought to be good, so the proposal for the agency went ahead . . .'.[6]

George Keightley, Marshall's senior representative for the Midlands and South-West England.

There were other considerations, not the least being the possibility that agents might start up in competition. The Royal Commission on the Depression of Trade and Industry reported that 'Umrath and Company in Prague, formerly the agents of Robey's of Lincoln, are now manufacturing all classes of agricultural machinery themselves in Prague'. Again, but in Budapest, the firm of Grossman's, formerly the agents of Ransomes and Head of Ipswich, were now manufacturing portable engines and thrashing machines, whilst Marshall's representative was manufacturing corn grinding mills and other agricultural implements.[7]

Another eventuality to be guarded against was the possibility that competitors might try to change the allegiance of agents by enticing them away from their 'parent' suppliers. Against the background of the highly competitive nature of the steam thrashing trade in Lincoln, Ruston Proctor went to extraordinary lengths to conceal the identity of their agents. One of the company's former representatives recalled that throughout the works the company's agents were known by numbers, and only at the last moment were the names and addresses added to consignments. Such concern was understandable, bearing in mind the

A Fowell traction engine thrashing at Guilden Morden, Cambridgeshire, in the early 1900's.

not inconsiderable investment involved, for many of Ruston Proctor's agents employed Ruston mechanics. Later it became the custom for agents to send their own staff to Lincoln for training.[8]

An agent with international connections was Agar, Cross and Company Limited, who were Ruston's sole agents for steam thrashing machinery in Argentina. Founded in Glasgow in 1884, the senior partners were Malcolm Cross and Richard, James and Thomas Agar, the latter partner also being the Argentine Republic's Consul-General for Scotland. The company's business was described as 'Commission Agents and Merchants', and as such they were basically concerned with selling into the North and South American markets. Branches were opened in Buenos Aires and New York, a London office being established between 1905 and 1908, whilst the Argentinian operation was subsequently strengthened with four strategic outlets at Rosario, Mendoza, Bhía Blanca and Tucumán.

Agar Cross were one of the major importing houses in Argentina and a comprehensive range of products was sold to meet the enormous demand for agricultural, industrial and domestic goods as the country developed.

Traction engine with crane working at the Agar Cross warehouse in Buenos Aires in 1927.

A corner of the Agar Cross showrooms in Buenos Aires.

At their large and impressive Buenos Aires branch, four floors of showrooms and galleries displayed, amongst other items, traction engines, thrashing machines and harvesting machinery. Extensive warehouses on the outskirts of Buenos Aires provided facilities for traction engine and thrashing machine assembly prior to delivery to the farmers and estate owners up-country.

Quite possibly Ruston Proctor's links with Agar Cross stemmed from the year of the latter's inception and they handled a wide variety of Ruston's products. From the literature which survives, and as far as steam thrashing machinery is concerned, it can be deduced that Agar's sales pitch in 1928 was slanted towards the 55 h.p. compound straw-burning outfit. This was towards the end of the steam era, but the dimensions of their trade in earlier years can be seen from the fact that in 1909, 1,171 Ruston Proctor thrashing machines were at work out of the Argentinian total of 5,600. Author Richard Brooks tells us in his book *Lincolnshire Engines Worldwide* that at least 990 Ruston Proctor traction engines were sold to Agar between 1903 and 1913.

Agar Cross also distributed thrashing machines and traction engines for the American concerns Avery and Advance Rumely.

Evidence of this once-substantial trade between Lincoln and Buenos Aires continues to survive in the form of silver medallions which were struck by Agar Cross in Buenos Aires in 1910. The medallions commemorate the exhibition held in that year at the Argentine Rural Society's grounds in Palermo in connection with the centenary of the Argentine: they were presented to customers visiting the Ruston Proctor machinery stand. Time notwithstanding, three of the 500 medallions produced are still in existence in England.

To complete the record, it remains to say that the U.K. operation of Agar Cross was acquired by Avdel plc of Welwyn Garden City and became a dormant company in 1982.[9]

*Photograph of the silver medallion which was struck
by Agar Cross in 1910. The medallion depicts a
Ruston Proctor straw-burning traction engine.*

CHAPTER V

George Thurlow and Sons Limited

At this point we continue to explore the commercial aspects of the steam
thrashing trade by turning to George Thurlow and Sons Limited, one of the
country's leading agents. In common with the larger builders of steam thrashing
machinery, Thurlow's too were based in Eastern England, at Stowmarket in
Suffolk. However, Thurlow's were very much more than agents: their interests
included the manufacture of belting, oil blending, the supply of requisites and at
a later date agricultural engineering and the manufacture of implements.

Since Thurlow's connections with the steam thrashing trade are interwoven
with their history we will begin by looking at the company's origins.

The founder was George Thurlow Senior, who was born at Leiston in Suffolk
on 1st June, 1837. Between 1864 and 1867 he moved to Stowmarket, and
although the actual date of the founding of the company has eluded the Author,
by 1875 he had set up in business as an oil merchant. Throughout the following
twenty-five years, George Thurlow Senior oversaw the growth of the company,
opening a belting factory and introducing machinery sales by 1879, whilst a
range of engine requisites were on the market by 1885.[1]

George Thurlow Senior had three sons. John, the eldest, entered the business
as an apprentice in 1875 and was later joined by his younger brother, George
Reeder Thurlow. During their leisure time, both John and George were keen
sportsmen and prize-winning racing cyclists throughout Suffolk, Essex, Norfolk
and Lincolnshire. The relevance of this is that their love of cycling and
knowledge of the area had a direct bearing on their appointments as the
company's representatives, for in those days cycling was one of the most
effective ways of visiting farmers deep in the heart of the countryside. Looking
back, one might speculate that this was also crucial in determining the lines
along which Thurlow's developed, for it was precisely in these self-same
counties that so much of John Thurlow's business originated. In addition to
promoting oil and belting, he developed contacts with the steam thrashing
machinery manufacturers: numbering amongst his close associates were several
members of the Garrett family, Marshall's Midlands Representative George
Keightley and Ruston Proctor's East Anglian Machinery Representative,

58

William Whinney. Through his travels John Thurlow became well known and it was said that '. . . many, and interesting were the stories that "Jack" Thurlow could tell of his adventures whilst working the East Coast . . .'[2]

John Thurlow became the manager of the company after his father's death in 1890 and both he and his brother effectively managed the concern. John continued to travel, as indeed did George, and before 1906 when the first motor car was purchased, George Thurlow travelled extensively to all parts of the country on his 'Invincible' Penny-farthing. Writing to the company in 1952, Mr. J. Percy Clover of Ipswich recalled a particular day in 1884 after his father had moved to Berkshire: apparently, George Thurlow '. . . turned up at Sindlesham on a Penny-farthing, and when surprise was affected at his call, said, "You were always a good customer so I followed you up" . . .'. This was typical of George Thurlow's business-like approach.

In 1903 the company became 'George Thurlow and Sons Limited', with George Thurlow as the managing director, a position he was to occupy for the next fifty years. Unfortunately the partnership with his brother came to an untimely end in 1906 when John Thurlow died at the early age of forty-four.

A Garrett set of thrashing tackle at an agricultural show in the early 1900s. Third and fourth from left: John Thurlow and George Reeder Thurlow.

George Thurlow was also a director and one-time chairman of Woods and Company (Stowmarket) Limited, the nearby implement and wagon builders at the Suffolk Iron Works. In 1914 he acquired Woods, extended his cramped premises and took on the manufacture of wagons, elevators, drills, harrows and a range of hand-powered machinery bearing the 'Woods' name. All of these together with a growing range of boiler fittings and sundries were marketed through catalogues and by this time Thurlow's could supply anything from an oil-can to a traction engine – in fact, virtually everything that could possibly be wanted by the engine or thrashing machine owner. As part of their service to the trade a complimentary handbook was produced in 1899 entitled *Traction Engine Law*, which was '. . . for the use of those engaged in working traction engines, road locomotives and road rollers . . .'. Another promotional item was a money wallet, blocked in gold 'With the compliments of G. Thurlow and Sons Ltd, Stowmarket 1918'.

A sales force was recruited, covering the country and providing support at the numerous agricultural shows which had been a central feature of Thurlow's business since 1881. Such a hectic programme was made possible by packing the exhibition material in crates and shipping it from show to show by rail: the effectiveness of this medium can be seen in the spate of orders which followed, marked 'ex-Smithfield Show', 'ex-Royal Show', and so forth, and it is to the thrashing machinery which we will now turn.

Fortunately the 'Machinery Sales Daybooks' exist from July 1903 to October 1955, providing a unique snapshot of the agent's activities. Geographically, the focus of the machinery business centred on Essex, Suffolk, Cambridgeshire, Norfolk and Lincolnshire, but extended nationally from Aberdeen to Chichester, and from Yarmouth to Liverpool and Belfast. The range of Thurlow's services to the thrashing trade included the purchase and sale of new and second-hand engines and thrashing machines, together with hire and repair work. Any permutation was seemingly possible – hiring out engines and thrashing machines, hiring out drivers, driving engines from place to place, and attending sales on behalf of others. And here lay one of the strengths of the business which George Thurlow exploited to the full: a customer for a traction engine was also a potential customer for thrashing machinery and items such as oils and packings: each part of the business interacted in the other once George Thurlow was talking to the buyer.

In evaluating Thurlow's agent's business, the Author has been greatly assisted by the work of Harold Armstrong who has over forty years' service with the company. Extracts from his analysis, which is detailed in Appendix 'A', show that more Marshall traction engines and thrashing machines were sold than other make, followed by Burrell and Garrett for engines, and Clayton and Shuttleworth and Foster for thrashing machines.

Much of the success of the Thurlow brothers can be attributed to their ability to construct business deals tailored to meet the financial needs of their farming

Thurlow's marquee at the 1910 Suffolk Show at Stowmarket. Second and third from left: John Thurlow and George Reeder Thurlow.

One of Thurlow's Cambridgeshire customers, C. R. Pumfrey and Sons of Duxford, thrashing with Burrell number 3721 at Duxford. Pumfrey's placed an order with Thurlow's for a new Burrell in August 1916, and the engine is a 7 n.h.p. single cylinder, spring mounted on the hind axle. The driver is Charles Pumfrey.

clients. They provided hire-purchase agreements based on special terms of credit, meticulously arranged and precisely confirmed in letters at the outset. But these terms had to be strictly observed, and as Esmond Kimbell recalled, George Thurlow summed up one of his rules for business in the simple maxim: '. . . Say what you'll pay, and pay what you say . . .'.

As an alternative to cash for the initial payment, old engines or thrashing machinery were accepted and in both cases the balance might typically be arranged in the form of monthly installments charged at 5% interest. Discounts of 2½%, 5% and occasionally 15% were allowed when the total purchase price was paid at the time of placing the order and sometimes there was the occasional copper top, belt or lamps 'thrown-in'.

In these ways, the farmer obtained a deal to suit his pocket, George Thurlow and the manufacturer secured a sale, and the manufacturer was relieved of the time-consuming business of arranging finance and selling second-hand engines. George Thurlow made it work through his tight control of contracts and his personality is indelibly stamped on the annotations to the Daybooks.

From the customer's point of view, the attractions of using an agent hinged not only on the deal he obtained, for when buying a set of thrashing tackle he faced an enormous choice of options. Should he buy a Marshall or a Burrell engine, a Clayton or a Garrett drum, a Maynard or an Innes chaff-cutter, or a Ruston or a Foden baler? George Thurlow advised, having prices, catalogues and 'the ear of the manufacturer'. Furthermore, Thurlow's could carry out those minor but nonetheless important modifications such as casting machine pulleys and fitting horse-shafts to thrashing machinery.

All these arrangements and facilities extended to the thriving second-hand market: items were taken in part-exchange for further second-hand equipment and, where necessary, reconditioned for re-sale. Amongst the customers and suppliers in the second-hand market there were several instances of trading between agents. For example, in 1906 Thurlow's bought a second-hand Burrell standing at Burrell's works at Thetford and sold it to another agent, James Graven of Ely.

Occasionally Thurlow's received orders from their suppliers. In 1904 they assisted Garrett's by supplying them with a Maynard chaff-cutter at 'Cost Price' to make up an otherwise all-Garrett set of thrashing tackle for Mr. Davey at Laxfield. And in 1912, Thurlow's invoiced Maynard's for '. . . £2. 0s. 0d. for 2 days use of engine for driving Chaff cutter at Suffolk Show at Stowmarket. . .'.

If not despatched from the manufacturer, engines were either driven to their destination or sent by rail from Stowmarket station. Sometimes the occasional 'hiccup' arose en route: on 10th April, 1905, the Great Eastern Railway were invoiced by Thurlow's for '. . . damage to traction engine from Wellington to Stowmarket ex: F. Payne. Damage to lagging of engine, and front steering chain, and steering gear broken, 3 spuds lost and one lamp broken and damage to boiler plate: £12. 0s. 0d.'.

Some notable engines passed through Thurlow's hands – a Stanford portable engine, traction engines built by Holmes of Norwich and Fyson of Soham, and on 11th June, 1932, the company handled the sale of the last Burrell, number 4094, which was built by Garrett's.

Turning to engine and machinery repair, Thurlow's had a small two-bay factory-style workshop, a machine shop, blacksmith's shop and sawmill. Some of the largest engineering jobs which the firm tackled were the rebuilding of single cylinder Fowler ploughing engines incorporating redesigned boilers supplied by the Oxfordshire Steam Ploughing Company. Using their 'improved late 14 h.p. boilers' as the basis, the 'new' engines were constructed using 'Oxford' fittings and practice, including radical alterations to the valve gear. Several sets were rebuilt from 1911, and the copious, long-hand descriptions in the Daybook provide a glimpse of Thurlow's repair facilities – the work included 'riveting by hydraulic machines', and, perhaps surprisingly, the use of oxy-acetelyne welding.

After the First World War the Daybook entries reflect the changing pattern of business. Sales of new traction engines dropped from twenty-two in 1920 to single figures thereafter and the last new steam thrashing set was despatched to J. Nott and Son, of Bradford, near Tiverton, in August 1935. The outfit consisted of a 6 h.p. Marshall single cylinder traction engine number 87002 with a Clayton thrashing machine and Hornsby trusser. However, the second-hand trade in engines continued until 1942 when 7 h.p. single crank compound Burrell number 2459 was repaired and sold to W. and T. Howling of Ingoldisthorpe, near King's Lynn.

Engine repair work continued both in the yard and 'on site'. John Tester remembers driving the Burrell-trained boilermaker 'Lennie' Barnes to Doran's yard at Thetford where they both re-tubed a steam roller in 1952. Three years later in June and July 1955 the final thrashing machines were delivered, a Ransomes and a Foster, whilst in a corner of the works a Burrell Showman's Engine languished before being towed away for scrap. All in all, some 368 new traction engines and 865 new thrashing machines were supplied between July 1903 and 1935 and 1955 respectively.

The company still enjoyed close ties with the thrashing trade and in 1948 George Thurlow was re-elected president of the National Traction Engine and Tractor Association. By then in his 'eighties', he continued to take a deep interest in the company until his death in 1952.

Although strictly outside the steam thrashing era, it is interesting to note that George Thurlow is still a flourishing family business, now controlled by the original George Thurlow's great-grandson, John Thurlow. The company is still very much in the agricultural machinery supply trade, holding major franchises, including Massey Ferguson in Suffolk, Norfolk and Cambridgeshire, together with a number of motor car franchises.[3]

PART THREE

CHAPTER VI

The late George Cox and Ruston's

George Cox's childhood co-incided with the ascendant years of the steam thrashing era. Born in 1902, his ambition to become involved with the industry was achieved in 1916 when he began his career with Ruston Proctor. The story of how he joined the company, and his subsequent experiences, proved to be enduring memories and it is upon his recollections of these years that this chapter is mainly based.

From the vicinity of Bury St. Edmunds in the early 1900s the family moved to Thetford. Here George's walk to school quite frequently included a detour past Burrell's works where as often or not he saw a new engine setting out on the trial run to Croxton. Later, the family moved to Somersby, about twenty-five miles east of Lincoln, where his father became the squire's gamekeeper. It was not long before George struck up a friendship with Jim and Alf Pepper of Hagworthingham who ran a Clayton and Shuttleworth set. Under their eyes his interest blossomed and one day he drove the tackle home after a spell of band-cutting in 1915.

To a schoolboy the possibility of owning a traction engines was remote, and as George himself put it: '. . . I had no hope of owning a traction engine, large or small, as my total assets were about fourpence. But Jim gave me four catalogues, an Allchin, two Clayton's and a Ruston, and the illustrations gave me the idea of making a small model . . .'. With the encouragement of Jim and his friends the project gradually took shape and was completed six months later – engine, drum and elevator, fashioned from metal and wood.

In July 1916, George left school at the age of fourteen but had no immediate job in prospect. Perhaps not unnaturally, his mother suggested that he should help his father around the farm and estate. One day, whilst out with his father and the squire, the subject of the models cropped up. Evidently impressed with George's ability, the squire felt that '. . . the boy should be put to engineering . . .'.

This was all very well, but in those days this was not so easy as it sounds, as his father well knew, for there was the financial aspect to consider and the family were many miles away from the nearest engineering centre at Lincoln.

However, George's mother thought that they should persevere and that the squire 'had something in mind'. Returning a few days later, the squire broke the news that he had spoken to the directors of Ruston Proctor and that they would like to see George with his thrashing set.

The squire provided a car and chauffeur, the local carpenter built a box for the models, and one morning during October both George and his mother set off on their first trip in a motor car to travel to the 'Sheaf Iron Works' at Lincoln.

On arrival they were shown into the offices to meet Colonel Ruston, the chairman, August Bornemann, the managing director, Howard Livens, the chief engineer, and Mr. G. H. Blow, the company secretary. One can well imagine George's feelings at meeting the 'top brass'. George remembered that: '. . . they asked me several questions in a kindly way about the models and appeared very pleased. Although the drum and elevator were clearly based on Clayton machines, this did not seem to bother them. By way of encouragement, Mr. Bornemann told me that as a boy he had sold matches in the streets of Amsterdam. I still regard these men as giants. I was a little over-awed by it all as we returned home . . .'.

Later, the family heard of the directors' plan. George was offered an apprenticeship, but before starting in the works he was to go to Lincoln Technical College for two years 'to learn some science'. The company would pay all the expenses for lodging and fees, and as George reflected: '. . . that is the kind of people they were . . .'.

George went to Lincoln in November, and for the next two years studied maths, chemistry and physics against the background of a Lincoln flat-out on munitions work. By now, Ruston Proctor employed over 7,600 at their five Lincoln factories – the Iron Works, Wood Works, Boiler Works, Navvy Works and the Aircraft Works. The Sheaf Iron Works was the head office and the department where the traction engines, portable engines and steam rollers were built.

However, the order of things was to be changed and events took a turn when Richard Hornsby of Grantham approached Ruston Proctor about the possibility of a merger in April 1918. The outcome was that Ruston Proctor took over Richard Hornsby and created the new concern of Ruston and Hornsby Limited in September 1918.[1] With over 10,600 employees the company ranked as one of the larger engineering concerns in the U.K.

A few weeks after the end of the war, George began his apprenticeship in the works. One can picture George on his first day – perhaps a little apprehensive, but probably pleased that at last he would be getting to grips with the practical side of engine building. Starting in the 'Brass Gallery', George ground-in plug-cocks, water-gauges, check valves, whistles and displacement lubricators – all formed part of a varied assortment of work. Once familiar with these tasks, he qualified for piecework and could earn about two pounds per week.

This was obviously 'production work', and looking back from today's sophisticated training schemes one has to bear in mind that there were few

The Boiler Shop at Ruston and Hornsby Limited in 1920.

The Road Roller Erection Shop at Ruston and Hornsby Limited in 1920.

apprentice training schools, skills were usually learnt 'on the job'. Nonetheless for that, there were opportunities to progress. If an apprentice was prepared to study in his own time and attend evening classes there was a strong likelihood that he would be chosen for entry to the Drawing Office or Design Department and he would be given an all-round training including pattern-making, turning and so forth. This was precisely the path that George followed, and during his career at Ruston's he worked in both of these departments and by dint of considerable studying over the years he gained a university degree and qualified as a Chartered Engineer.

George did a fair amount of fitting work on traction engines during his apprenticeship but to preserve sequence we must first turn to the 'new' boiler works which was built in 1903. Here George's over-riding impressions were of the sheer scale of the machinery and the noisy atmosphere. The sporadic clatter of riveting, the discords of planers and air tools, all combined in a cacophony of sound against the background roar of furnaces. For here in the course of production were large Lancashire and Cornish boilers, locomotive boilers for the Great Western and the L.M.S., and smaller boilers for portables, rollers and tractions – an assorted output of about forty boilers per week.[2]

After riveting and machining the seating for the cylinder, boilers for tractions, portables and rollers were hauled the half-mile or so to the erecting shops by one of the three steam tractors. This was where the intricacies of crankshaft and cylinder fitting occurred before the erection of the engine proper, a task which was usually more straightforward although there were keys to be fitted and the bedding of the weighshaft bracket to the boiler.

On to lagging and painting, and through a change in lodgings George met Jim Baldry, the landlady's son, who was a 'Liner' in the Paint Shop. Watching him at work – and learning one or two 'tricks of the trade' in the process – George cast his mind back to periodic visits to the Portable Test Shop: the foreman was a golfer, and sometimes two or three golf balls were being whitened!

When George finished his apprenticeship the post-war recession was under way and the demand for traction engines was dwindling. From the manufacturer's point of view, Ruston and Hornsby were expanding in the oil-engine market and moving away from steam thrashing machinery. During 1919 they acquired a controlling interest in Ransomes, Sims and Jefferies of Ipswich and as part of their policy of concentrating on the oil-engine transferred their agricultural business to Ipswich. Possibly Ruston and Hornsby finished making traction engines at Lincoln in 1928, although during that year there were a number of standard and 'Light-type' engines in stock which were being offered for sale at reduced prices.

It therefore came as something of a surprise to George when he was asked to carry out some traction engine work in 1935. At the time he was working in the Traction Drawing Office, now given over largely to oil-engined locomotives, when his colleague requested some modifications to two traction engines which had been in stock since 1928. The engines concerned bore the numbers 175054 and 175055, and were 'Light Agricultural Traction Engines' designed for the Baltic States. They were to be exported, and George had to devise a way of making the safety-valves tamperproof. This was not so easy as it sounds, as George well knew through his earlier experiences of traction engine drivers and their resourcefulness. After various alternatives were drawn up, the fittings were passed out by the Erecting Shop foreman and both engines were sold to Herren Woldemar Major of Latvia on the 26th June, 1935. As such, they are believed to be the last two traction engines of the Ruston lineage.

Having a last look at the engines, George's colleague suggested that it would be a nice gesture if George could build a model to commemorate Ruston's traction engine activities: of course at that time, in 1935, neither could foresee the burgeoning of the preservation movement. George took the suggestion as a great compliment and they returned to the drawing office where a search revealed some of the standard traction engine drawings.

The Ruston class 'SLB' designed for the Baltic States. The last four Ruston tractions were the 17 b.h.p. version and George Cox modified the safety valves on the final two engines which were despatched in June 1935.

As it happened, George himself left Rustons shortly afterwards to join the British Thomson-Houston Company. But the challenge of constructing the model was never very far from his mind and during the following years he sought out Ruston traction engines wherever they stood, meticulously noting and sketching details.

Work started on the single cylinder agricultural engine in 1942. Using and adapting an old 3" treadle lathe in his workshop 'upstairs', George carefully built an exact replica of the Ruston and Hornsby 7 n.h.p. class 'SH', even adopting the traditional pattern of boiler plating and riveting. After completion in 1951, George decided to build a scale version of the 54" thrashing machine and 22' Hayes-pattern elevator, the thrashing machine being, if anything, the most difficult task of all. Such was his pursuit of authenticity that with the engine belted up and with the problems overcome he was able to thrash a mixture of plantain seed and dry grass.

After his retirement in 1968, George constructed a true-to-scale 7 n.h.p. Ruston and Hornsby compound agricultural engine and the once-numerous 'Champion' clover huller. All of his models bear the hallmark of technical accuracy and the uncompromising reproduction of intricate detail. Indeed, it has been remarked that George succeeded in portraying that indefinable aura of the working scene, expressing his understanding of the subtleties of thrashing gained from both the factory and the field.

George Cox died in 1995. His experience and achievements reflect yet another aspect of the human affairs of the steam thrashing era. The amalgam of steam thrashing, engineering and model-making formed an abiding interest for George, who was not one in any sense to seek recognition. It is fitting that his models will stand as a tangible memory.

George Cox (extreme right) with his Ruston and Hornsby traction engine, thrashing machine and Hayes-pattern elevator.

CHAPTER VII

Contracting

The Implement and Machinery Review pointed out that before the First World War, it was not uncommon for contractors to purchase four-fifths of the thrashing machines which were sold for use in the U.K., whereas farmers purchased one-fifth.[1]

In other words, ownership of a thrashing machine – and the engine to drive it – was regarded as an uneconomic proposition by a large section of the farming community. That this should be so need not surprise us when it is remembered that the cost of an engine and thrasher represented a considerable expenditure for the limited working season which was available. Hiring a contractor provided the usual alternative under the prevailing conditions of the time.[2]

From the contractor's standpoint, the move into contracting sometimes arose from established links with farming: typically, a farmer with his own thrashing set 'filling out the season' by working for his neighbours. He might combine this with engine work 'out of season', or, not to mince matters, with whatever engine work could be found.

Contracting took many forms. The Author researched Joseph Griffin's business, including the thrashing round to which Esmond Kimbell contributes.

Bob Griffin recalled that his father Joseph, who lived at Bruern Grange in Oxfordshire, bought the first thrashing set with which he established his business in 1916. This was a second-hand Ransomes steam tractor and Humphries thrashing machine from Rowell's of Chipping Norton. Although the tackle was primarily for use on his three large farms, Joseph began to thrash for others. The outfit was completed with a wagon, built by a local wheelwright, and after tea each day Joseph hauled the sacks of grain to Matthew's Mill at Shipton railway station. Truly a 'maid-of-all-work', the Ransomes was used at other times for direct-traction ploughing, and it was by no means uncommon for 28-acre fields to be worked in this manner.

During these wartime years there was a large demand for pressed hay for feeding the horses in service with the British Army in France. A baler was acquired, and in 1918 an old Fowler traction engine and thrasher were purchased, again from Rowell's of Chipping Norton. Joseph also supplied baled hay and cut chaff for Birmingham Co-operative Society's van horses. This was a trade which persisted for a number of years and proved to be highly popular, providing an outlet for the farm and work for the thrashing engines.

The war over, Joseph decided to buy a set of steam ploughing tackle. This was not a step to be taken lightly: there were several well-established concerns in the region – such as the Oxfordshire Steam Ploughing Company – and the high capital cost tended to favour the concentration of ploughing sets in the hands of the larger contractors. For £4,999, Joseph purchased two brand-new ploughing engines and their implements from John Fowler and Company of Leeds. After receiving the 'full treatment' at the Steam Plough Works, they were sent to the Royal Show at Cardiff before delivery to the Fifield farm where the engines were kept. As was usual on these occasions, one of Fowler's men travelled down to train the thrashing drivers and supervise the handling of the tackle.

The introduction of steam ploughing augered well for the thrashing engine drivers. The perennial problem which plagued many thrashing businesses – that of providing work during the summer months – was now eased. Since the ploughing season occupied the summer months, Joseph could now provide continuous employment for a number of the thrashing engine drivers at the end of their season, thereby keeping the skilled team together.

By way of comparison, Esmond Kimbell's experience in Northamptonshire was that '. . . Steam ploughing did keep the men more regularly employed but there was overlap at harvest time, with difficulty in spacing the men out. Those brought up to steam ploughing were seldom happy with thrashing, although thrashing men were the better, the other way round – providing they kept their rope from cutting a groove on a front wheel. An alternative to steam ploughing was steam rolling for tar sprayers, which had a shorter season . . .'.

At its peak, Joseph Griffin's farming and contracting employed 25 men and boys with a stable of 26 horses. Although a certain amount of steam ploughing was carried out at the home farms, which now totalled some 920 acres, the tackle was mostly out on contract, and here Joseph's acquaintance with the local farmers stood him in good stead. Work for the ploughing and thrashing engines very often resulted from his weekly meetings at Kingham market and in this way Joseph kept in touch with the local scene and built up a useful round in the neighbourhood.

On through the 1920s, which were, surprisingly, a time of growth for Joseph Griffin, despite the depression of the post-war years. Once a circle of customers had been established for the ploughing tackle, Joseph turned again to thrashing, which was always his principal activity, and began to expand with a Fowler traction engine and a thrashing machine from Frank Reading near Leamington in 1925. The following year he acquired a Wantage traction engine and Clayton and Shuttleworth thrashing machine from Mr. Woolcock's sale at nearby Chadlington.

The arrival of the next engine for thrashing occurred in 1928 and was will

Joseph Griffin's first engine, Ransomes steam tractor number 26813. Photographed whilst thrashing at Hill Farm, Fifield, in 1917.

The staff of Joseph Griffin's business in 1929. Front row, second and fourth from left: Mervyn and Bob Griffin. Back row, first from left: Joseph Griffin.

remembered by nine-year-old Bob. One day in June his father took him to Shipton station to unload a Ransomes steam tractor which had arrived from Nottingham on a flat truck. This engine had caught Joseph's eye whilst visiting the Royal Show, and he bought it straight off the maker's stand. Costing him £320, the Ransomes proved to be a handy little engine with a fair turn of speed and was ideally suited to stackyards and narrow lanes 'off the beaten track'.

The thrashing process demanded a competent team. There were 'tricks of the trade' – and regional variations – even in the apparently straight-forward task of 'feeding'. 'In Lincolnshire, they fed by hand', recalled Esmond Kimbell, 'wheat sheaves across the drum-mouth, over the arm, whilst barley was held "heads down", easier to feed with a little always left in the hand to "even out the hum" before the next sheaf. In Northamptonshire there were more thistles, so feeding was mostly by fork, sometimes twisted upwards to spread the sheaf out. Practice brought skill here so the engine's chuffs could be as regular as those in Lincolnshire. With beans, a hood went over the feed hole to keep the bouncing-back ones in'.

Bob Griffin, as a 'junior' member of the team, often followed the progress of the thrashing and ploughing sets on his bike, spending as much time as he could with the drivers. The occasional spell on the footplate was not unknown, and in Bob's own words, '. . . When I was ten, I first handled an engine under the guidance of the driver, but was very soon left to it . . .'. Of such material are budding drivers made, and it came as no surprise to those who knew him to learn that after leaving Burford Grammar School at the age of sixteen, he started work as 'cook boy' with the ploughing tackle. Throughout the next two years he worked his way up to become an engine driver, thereby gaining a rise in pay from five to thirty-two shillings per week, plus 'acreage' money.

Steam ploughing usually occurred within 20 miles of Fifield. 'On the road', the leading engine hauled the plough and cultivator, followed by the second engine with the living van and water cart. Five men formed the crew – two drivers, a ploughman and the cook boy, with the foreman in overall charge. Between them, ploughing was carried out continuously by changing around through the meal breaks, for it was a very keen market and payment was partly by piecework, or what was known as 'acreage money'. The drivers could earn an extra 'threepence per single acre, once over', or 'sixpence per double acre, twice over'.

On returning to the yard at the end of August it was very often a case of 'out with the four thrashing sets'. The Wantage was Bob's particular engine and he recalled a troublesome day in 1936.

At the time, he was thrashing at Taynton, in the Windrush valley near Burford. Biking over as usual, he had steam up by 7 o'clock and set off with the thrashing machine and baler to a nearby farm. It was raining heavily when he changed gear and turned off the road to begin the mile-long climb along the stone cart track. With the engine working hard he eventually had no alternative other than to winch the tackle up the track in stages.

The 1928 Ransomes steam tractor, number 39088, about to set off from Fifield with a Ruston baler and thrashing machine in 1944. From left to right: Claud Ricketts, driver, and David Patrick.

This took most of the day and it was dark when Bob got to the rick-yard, so he had to set-up by the light of oil lamps. As if this was not enough, he noticed more than the usual amount of steam coming from the chimney and realised that the tubes were leaking.

Deciding to put matters right, Bob cycled the four miles home to collect his tools. With the engine still warm, he dropped the ashpan and firebars to expand the tubes, and for good measure re-leaded the fusible plug.

Filling up the boiler and re-assembling, he lit the fire and 'banked up' ready for the morning, then back home again at 12 o'clock for a few hours' sleep before rising at 4.30 to get his food ready. Finally off to Taynton for what was to prove to be a trouble-free day's thrashing – a satisfactory outcome to his earlier endeavours.

Bob took occasions such as these in his stride, and as a fully-fledged contractor viewed the thrashing round in a routine manner.

The objective of producing a 'clean' sample of grain involved a number of skills. Part of what was entailed may interest the reader, and was explained to the Author by Esmond Kimbell: '. . . One looked for enginemanship and

Fowler 'K7' ploughing engine, number 15270, hauling the cultivator and harrow near Enstone in Oxfordshire in 1932.

The engine yard at Hill Farm, Fifield, in 1928. Engines, front row, left to right: Fowler 6 n.h.p., Wantage 8 n.h.p. No. 1522, Fowler 6 n.h.p. No. 7914; background: Ransomes steam tractor, 4 n.h.p. No. 39088 and Fowler ploughing engines Nos. 15270 and 15271.

thrashing machine skills – balancing the adjustments for concave, blowers and screens – according to the crop to be thrashed. Good driving was essential: steam pressure and governing had to be steady – overspeeding increased the air which could blow away a light grain like oats. With beans, the concave was opened out so that it was "shelling" rather than "thrashing".'

The year 1936 marked the Griffin's purchase of the last set of thrashing tackle, an Aveling and Porter traction engine and a Ruston and Hornsby thrashing machine from Mr. Fowler, a farmer at Taston. In 1938, the ninth and final engine was bought from the sale of Wilder's of Wallingford – a Fowler ploughing engine rebuilt by Wilder's using parts from John Allen of Oxford. Joseph particularly wanted this engine because it could be used 'left-hand' or 'right-hand' to match either of his ploughing engines in the event of a breakdown: all that had to be done was to 'swing the blocks over'. (Joseph Griffin's engines are detailed in Appendix 'B'.)

This takes us up to 1939, and against the background of a troubled Europe, Joseph decided to stock-up with all the spare parts he could obtain. At the same time, Bob himself overhauled one of the ploughing engines, whilst the other was driven over to Kingham to receive similar treatment at the works of E. J. Lainchbury and Sons.

Joseph's foresight was rewarded. With the opening up of large tracts of land, Bob and his men worked continuously on ploughing, cultivating and thrashing for the War Agricultural Committees. In fact Bob, who was appointed foreman at the early age of 23, regarded the war-time years as the busiest he could remember. From Evesham in the north, to Highworth in the south, about 40 miles, the roads were traced and retraced. During one six-month period in 1943, the team worked in five different counties and ploughed 1,600 acres, often working up to 17 hours a day. Sometimes Bob worked until 4 o'clock in the morning to carry out essential repairs, but throughout the war he only had to bring the tackle home once.

And yet despite all this activity, the war to all intents and purposes 'saw steam out'. After the autumn of 1945, Bob could not find a single customer for steam ploughing. Thrashing by steam finished slightly earlier, at the end of 1944, and a complement of tractors were used until the introduction of combine harvesters in 1953.

Looking back, Bob has few regrets: '. . . it was a tough life, but I enjoyed it all . . .'. He later took up farming and ran a machine shop, but steam was never far from his thoughts and until recently he owned and restored a Fowler ploughing engine which occasionally carried out the odd day's work. Now in retirement, he has a wealth of memories to draw on, and is never happier than when talking about 'steam'.

Bob Griffin with 'Ajax' in 1976.

CHAPTER VIII

The late Henry Marshall

This chapter is about the late Henry Marshall, and brings together the family, the firm and the story of Henry Marshall's involvement with steam thrashing.

Henry Marshall was born in the steam thrashing era, in 1910, and as many enthusiasts will know he was the great-grandson of William Marshall, the founder of Marshall, Sons and Company Limited.

In the year that Henry was born the company was experiencing a period of almost unbridled expansion. Despite the increasing competition overseas, the firm had almost doubled in size during the previous eighteen years. Four thousand were employed at the thirty-nine acre Britannia and Trent Works where Henry's father, Herman Dickenson Marshall, was the director in charge of engineering and administrative affairs. For a number of years the family lived at Carr House, Gainsborough, in the precincts of the works, but moved to Pilham Hall in 1910.

Now most of the thrashing in Pilham was carried out by Messrs. T. H. and W. S. Clarke from the neighbouring village of Corringham, a fact that had not escaped the notice of youthful Henry. Steam thrashing intrigued him, and when he was five he often walked down the lanes to the nearby farms to track down 'Steve' – the driver – plying him with all manner of questions about how this or that was done. 'Steve' – or Mr. Stephenson, to give him his proper name – kept an eye on Henry and used to let him ride on the engine when passing Pilham Hall, where an appreciative father exchanged a few words for he approved of his son's budding interest.

Little did Henry realise that one day he would own the engine he was travelling on – number 45415, a single cylinder 1906 Marshall. Like many other children born in the age of steam, Henry wanted to be an engine driver. Under Mr. Stephenson's tuition and at the early age of six he drove the engine on the belt, firing and maintaining the water level and steam pressure. A year later he could start the engine without pulling the belt off, and when he was eight he could shunt around the stackyard and set to the drum with a reasonable amount of success.

This was a unique experience for a boy interested in thrashing, apart from being a useful introduction to life in general, and provided a welcome change from Uppingham, the school which he joined as a boarder at the age of eight. During the next few years he always managed to spend as much of his holidays as possible with Mr. Stephenson and the tackle.

Leaving Uppingham at the age of eighteen-and-a-half, and bearing in mind his interests, it was perhaps natural that he decided to join the family firm. It was agreed that his training should be aimed at giving him a thorough grounding in the business 'from the bottom up', so in the latter part of 1928 he began a five-year apprenticeship as a fitter and turner. At this time his father, who was shortly to become Chairman and Joint Managing Director, was bringing the works up-to-date and had an immediate project for Henry – '. . . You've got to learn more about tooling, my boy'. With these words ringing in his ears, Henry was sent to one of the leading machine tool makers, Alfred Herbert of Coventry. This culminated in extensive sales of capstan lathes and 'automatics' to Marshall's.

Returning some eighteen months later, Henry embarked on the second part of his apprenticeship and started working in the machine shop from the 1st December, 1929. Becoming assistant to the manager, Jim Gledhill, Henry put into practice the knowledge he had earlier gained.

A few words about the machine shop will not be out of place, for when it was built in 1905 it was reputed to be the largest in the world and even at this time during the 'Depression' years over two hundred were employed. And from another angle the machine shop has a claim to historical importance: in June 1905, before the machinery was installed, over seven thousand attended a political meeting at which Joseph Chamberlain addressed the issue of Tariff Reform.

Henry had good reason to remember the 1930s because, in his own words: '. . . I had a certain amount of licence as to what I did'. He was given a free hand to visit the other departments in the twenty-acre works which at that time was employing between two and three thousand. He was always on the look-out for a traction engine to test and whenever a new one was completed he used to give it a good run after steaming trials, driving up and down the road between Britannia Works and the Great Central station, the usual testing ground. On one occasion he had a narrow escape when a steering chain broke as he was reversing and the engine veered towards the works wall – had he not had the presence of mind to throw the reversing lever forward, he would have been cut in half.

Another job that Henry found very much to his liking was testing a thrashing drum, and of course a traction engine had to be found to drive it. All in all, Henry gleaned a great deal of knowledge during his 'roving commission' and he became conversant with all aspects of manufacture.

Traction engines were erected in the fitting shop by a three-man team. The senior fitter was in charge, accompanied by a 'fitter-learner' and a labourer to

Marshall's 1911 'Fen' traction engine – 5 n.h.p. single cylinder, lightweight hind wheels fitted with extensions, and boiler fitted with camber-top firebox.

A Marshall 'Gainsborough' light traction engine hauling a ten-furrow plough in Argentina in 1914.

fetch the parts, drawings and so forth. After assembly, initial steamings were carried out on the 'testing pits', followed by a spell on the dynamometer in the works yard when 'indicator diagrams' were taken, but at busy times when the dynamometer was occupied the age-old expedient of levering a stout plank under the flywheel was adopted.

Every engine was 'indicated' before delivery, valves and eccentric rods adjusted, the whole operation generally taking about half a day. After steaming trials, the engine was driven up to the loading sheds and onto the railway trucks which were shunted into Marshall's sidings and assembled into trains by the old tram engine.

There was much to interest the steam enthusiast in those days. Apart from the activities of the works departments there were, until 1930, three steam tractors shuttling between the Britannia, Trent and Carr House works, fetching and carrying supplies and parts with the occasional trip to Pilham Hall to deliver the coal and wood.

Quite frequently during these years – if not training with the Territorial Army – Henry would leave the works at five o'clock and rush up the hill to where Bradshaw's of Sturton-by-Stow were cultivating the 'strong land' at Gainsborough Hill Top. Henry was well-known to the drivers, who used to shout out: '. . . this is the best engine, come on this one . . .' and Henry took over the controls enabling the driver to leave early for home and for his tea. Henry recalled that this was lucky for him as he became quite popular with the crews.

Henry's father had a farm at Brandsby where the thrashing was invariably carried out with a 'works' engine, or one of Clarke's, and Henry used to take the engine over for the annual eight days' thrashing. On another occasion, a works engine was borrowed to carry out some thrashing at a farm which Henry's grandfather had previously owned at nearby Marton. On packing up, the steersman, Harry Good, fell off the thrashing machine and broke his collar bone. They had to get the engine back to the works that night, so there was nothing for it but for Harry to steer all the way back with one arm, visiting the doctor in the morning.

There were other links between Marshall's and the local thrashing scene. Whilst the Author and Henry were leafing through the engine registers, Henry spotted a 'Q'-class engine which he had seen at the works on several occasions. '. . . In 1914 we supplied this six-horse engine to Mr. Taylor of Tickhill', recalled Henry, '. . . and for five or six summers during the 1930s he regularly drove his engine into the works for overhaul. Quite a number of the local thrashing contractors brought their engines to us when they needed any major work done such as the fitting of a new firebox'.

It was as well that Henry made the most of these years because the days of steam thrashing were numbered. Between 1928 and 1930, production was running at about two portables, one steam roller and one traction per week, declining to six tractions throughout 1937 – a far cry from his father's

Tipping road stone in the vicinity of Marshall's works. One of Marshall's steam tractors heads the load.

recollections of seeing as many as twenty traction engines lined up on the testing pits. The final tractions and portables were despatched in 1940 and 1948, but thrashing machines continued on a reduced scale before rising to two thousand throughout the Second World War – more than half the total produced in the country.

In 1938, Henry became the manager of the machine shop, a position he occupied until the outbreak of war. He served as a major, re-joining Marshall's in 1946.

1948 was Marshall's centenary year: it also marked Henry's appointment as manager of the Tea Machinery Department and the first of a series of business trips to India and Pakistan. Six years later he became involved with the manufacture and testing of 750 steam rollers for India. These were built and tested at Gainsborough before being dismantled and shipped for re-erection.

With the resurgence of the interest in traction engines in the early 1950s, Henry wondered what had become of his favourite engine. He kept track of it during the war years and he knew that Mr. Stephenson's retirement had prompted the sale of the engine in 1945, the owner at that time being Mr. Shepherdson of North Owersby. As Henry later recalled in *Britannia News*, '. . . One evening in the winter of 1953 I drove up to North Owersby, some eighteen miles from my home to see if Mr. Shepherdson could tell me what had become of number 45415. It was quite dark when I arrived at his yard, but I could see a row of engines lined up, and you can imagine my feelings when he said that number 45415 was among them and in good going order. He was not too anxious to sell her to me, as he also liked her the best of his fleet which was then about six engines. However, we finally made a deal, and at last after many years the engine became mine, and indeed she still is'.[1]

About six weeks later, Henry steamed the engine home and he lost no time in restoring it to tip-top condition. He drove the engine into Marshall's works where a thorough overhaul was carried out before exhibiting on Marshall's stand at the 1954 Royal Show at Windsor.

It was now but a step to the traction engine rallies. Henry's desire to recreate the thrashing scene came to fruition when he acquired a full set of tackle – Marshall thrashing drum, Clayton chaff cutter, Cook's straw elevator and Massey tier. Thus equipped, he occasionally visited the local farms which he had visited so many years ago to carry out the odd day's thrashing.

Until the onset of ill-health, Henry continued to work at 'Marshall's' where he was also responsible for the company records. As an authority on the subject he received a thriving correspondence from enthusiasts the world over. His interest and friendship were widely appreciated, and although he died in 1993 he will undoubtedly be remembered by all who knew him in his many activities.

The 6 n.h.p. 'Q'-class traction engine manufactured by Marshall's.

A 1979 photograph of Henry Marshall and his thrashing outfit at Brandsby Farm, near Gainsborough.

PART FOUR

CHAPTER IX

Observations, 1914-1990

The crucial turning point of the steam thrashing trade pivoted upon the period of the First World War and the immediate aftermath. However, some of the factors which contributed to the decline of the 1920s and 1930s were already in place well before 1914; the war hastened the process. Technologically, the farm tractor was in its early stages of development, and the introduction of the 'stripper-harvester' foreshadowed the combined harvester-thrasher. As we have mentioned on more than one occasion, strong competition from North America and Germany had already made inroads, and the influence of political factors could be discerned in nationalistic tariffs in a number of the overseas markets.

From the manufacturers' point of view, the periodic occurrence of poor harvests served to emphasise the volatile nature of the thrashing trade, whilst the collapse of Clayton's Vienna operation acted as a harbinger of the possible fate of the Central and Eastern European business. Questionable was the future role of steam and thrashing – sooner or later, the next generation of products had to be considered. Diversification existed, but the prime task was to bring to fruition a product or range of products which could adequately replace steam thrashing.

With the outbreak of war, the resources of the Lincoln firms were channelled into ordinance and munitions production with the inevitable result that there was a withdrawal from overseas markets, an unfortunate consequence which materially affected post-war sales in these areas. In the short term, munitions and ordinance more than compensated for sales from peacetime overseas markets – in fact, one company chairman remarked that Lincoln workmen had never in their history been better employed.[1]

The flexibility and versatility of the Lincoln firms was amply demonstrated as they geared-up for wartime production and to enumerate all the items which were produced would be superfluous. Suffice to say that under Sir William Tritton's leadership Foster's introduced the Tank, whilst Robey, Ruston Proctor and Clayton's built aeroplanes.

During the latter part of the War, manufacture of agricultural machinery was increased to counteract the effects of the blockade of foodstuffs caused by the German submarine campaign. Along with the requirement for thrashing and baling machinery there was the need to plough-up thousands of acres of land for home food production. Steam tillage achieved the record figure of over one million acres during one of the war years,[2] but the sheer urgency and immensity of the task, together with the need to cultivate smaller and upland fields, demanded the employment of both horse and tractor draught.

As may be appreciated, in addition to the shortage of manpower there was a dearth of horses to pull the ploughs due to the needs of the British Army, whilst at the same time the fledgling British tractor industry was largely given over to munitions. It was to the United States that the Ministry of Munitions turned, and large numbers of farm tractors were imported. In this way, the American tractor builders gained a foothold in the British market: the thrust given to this competitor to steam due to wartime needs hastened the eventual demise of the portable and traction engine.

The transitory flush of orders on the home market, around 1919 and 1920, may have temporarily masked the onset of long-term decline. Compelling evidence about the state of post-war demand for agricultural machinery was presented by the Agricultural Engineers Association to the Committee on Industry and Trade in 1924. Based on a survey of 24 large firms manufacturing agricultural machinery, the A.E.A. revealed that 1923 output was less than half that of 1913, whilst export sales turnover had declined by 70%.[3]

The implications for the Lincoln manufacturers and the industry at large were inescapable. The export trade had always been the bedrock of the industry: home demand was too small to support large-volume production. With the decline in the major pre-war markets of Central and Eastern Europe and Argentina the very existence of the industry was called into question. Caught between over-capacity and declining markets the search for new markets and products was intensified.

Causes of the decline have been suggested earlier: to do justice to the facts requires a more detailed analysis than can be rendered here.

At home, during the inter-war years, the declining acreage under cereal crops reduced the demand for thrashing and hence the demand for contractors' services and manufacturers' products alike: both were squeezed by the effects of a diminishing market. Change was also precipitated by the wider use of the farm tractor for driving thrashing machines. Here the principal demand shifted from the medium and heavy machines to a lighter, cheaper machine which was developed to match the hauling and driving characteristics of the more 'modern' designs of lightweight tractors.[4]

Coupled together, the lower-cost tractor and tractor thrasher reached a wider farming fraternity than ever before, providing farmers with the opportunity of owning their own outfits and carrying out their thrashing independently of the contractor and at a time which suited.[5]

The trend towards farmer-owned thrashing sets totally changed the structure of the contracting business to the extent that by 1930, four-fifths of the thrashing

Working for the Army Service Corps: hauling baled hay for horse fodder in France. In 1917, the late Bob Pumfrey drives 'Success', the family's 7 n.h.p. Ruston Proctor No. 50278 (1914), hauling 17 tons of baled hay at Mildenhall station, Suffolk. C. R. Pumfrey and Sons gained the U.K. record when they baled 242 tons of hay in 97 hours with 'Success', a baler, and a seven-man team.

Charles Sumner and Sons' three Robey traction engines haul the entire equipment of a Lincolnshire farm from Bloxholme to the Doncaster area. Bertram Sumner stands by the hind wheel of the first engine.

machines sold in the U.K. were bought by farmers, one-fifth by contractors, a complete inversion of the situation prevailing before the First World War.[6]

Apart from farmer-owned and tractor-powered thrashers, the steam thrashing contractor also had to contend with inflationary pressures. By 1920, the price of a 7 n.h.p. single cylinder thrashing set had risen to around £1,700 (compared with £600-£700 pre-war), whilst wages, consumables and repairs had increased accordingly. These were some of the points which were introduced by Arthur Cole at a meeting of the National Traction Engine Owners and Users Association in 1920.

Attention inevitably focused on the prices charged to farmers and it emerged that there were wide variations in the trade at large. Instances were cited where prices had been pared to 'get the work regardless': indeed, Arthur Cole observed that very few owners of thrashing tackle really knew what their daily running costs were.

These unpalatable facts provided the stimulus for a nationwide campaign to acquaint the trade with the financial position and to negotiate increases by working though the affiliated local or county associations. The National Traction Engine Owners and Users Association recommended a blanket increase of at least 20% and the county associations negotiated tariffs for the various thrashing operations which were voluntarily applied by the local membership in their dealings with farmers. A framework was therefore provided for local charging, although in the final analysis there was little to prevent 'deals', whatever the status of the contractor.[7]

The realities were spelt out by Esmond Kimbell, who is now in his 90th year: '. . . In the 1920s and 1930s, prices were cut to ribbons and there were difficulties with payment. If you didn't "clean" the grain properly, or if there was too much grain left in the straw, then the farmer could threaten not to have you again . . .'!

The use of portable and traction engines declined from 3,731 in 1925 to 2,246 in 1931.[8] Three years later, the value of the production of steam thrashing sets had dropped to £27,000 from the pre-war 1913 figure of £2,250,000, a dramatic reduction whether inflation is taken into account or not.[9] Unrelieved decline was temporarily arrested during the Second World War – as in the First, dependency upon home-produced food was paramount and with it the need to open-up grain-growing land. Steam thrashing played its part, but on occasions the traction engine hauled the thrasher from farm to farm whilst the farmer provided a tractor to drive it.

The balance tilted in favour of the new competing prime movers. Esmond Kimbell chose Marshall 'Model M' diesel tractors, '. . . which were fitted with built-in winches, the total weight providing ample adhesion for hauling the tackle on the road. They were handier for thrashing than the later "Field Marshall", and with a larger thrashing drum pulley were quite strong enough, and unlike the paraffin tractors of the day, reliable starters. One winched everywhere on soft ground, easy enough with trailed anchor and man standing,

A cheerful gathering by the Foster thrashing set owned by Mr. Vesey of Keelby. Photographed at Linden's Farm, Riby, Lincolnshire, in 1933.

with seat off, so that he could get on and off easily. Men – ah! steam trained ones – were difficult to get, and some were vain and independent, whereas given basic common sense, getting a man into the way of tractor thrashing was easier, and the farmers preferred it . . .'.

These were the hard facts at the time, from an experienced operator and owner of both traction engines and tractors.

Esmond Kimbell kept in touch with Foster's, often visiting them for advice and to see old friends – a link which stemmed from his father's purchase of a thrashing set in the 1920s. One day, he wrote to Sir William Tritton about '. . . having seen a strange machine in a market place on my way home from Lincoln . . .'.

'. . . That', said Sir William, 'is a "Combine Harvester" and an attempt to out-date thrashing, but it is only suitable for a dry climate and will never take-on in this country . . .'!

In similar vein, Esmond Kimbell recalled the first British-built combine which was made by Clayton and Shuttleworth in 1930: '. . . this was bought by a retired Royal Navy engineer who took up farming in Hampshire. He used it for years and made it known in the farming press, praising its virtues – but it was ignored – until the war came . . .'.

Overtaken by farm tractors and the combine harvester, the end for steam thrashing was ragged. So far as the Author has been able to research, steam thrashing continued on a commercial basis in isolated pockets until the mid-1960s and there may well be later instances. Abroad, the process was longer-lived. In one country, steam thrashing was still being carried out in February 1990. Ian Thomson, who lives in Chile, discovered Ransomes portable engines driving thrashing machines at two locations in the south of the country, one in 1988 and one in 1990, and it is fortunate that he photographed and recorded these scenes.

These evocative events inevitably take us back to the export trade, and to the heyday of steam thrashing when through international trade the products of the industry ranged to the four corners of the world. With the development of engineering methods and management, production processes and costs were honed to the point where it was possible to build, ship and deliver large numbers of steam thrashing sets to compete in overseas markets many thousands of miles away. As such, this represented a continuing organisational effort – not to say teamwork – as manufacturers, shipping lines, railway companies and agents played their part at each stage in the lengthy chain from maker to user; it was also an achievement of which all could be justly proud.

Steam thrashing in Southern Chile in February 1990. Oxen transport the Antrillado family's wheat to a Chilean-built Morawitz thrasher which is driven by a Ransomes, Sims and Jefferies portable engine. The engine is number 32084, and is a 4 n.h.p. single cylinder.

101

References

Chapter I **Aspects of Lincoln's trade with Hungary and the rise of Hofherr Schrantz, 1852-1912**

1. '70 Éves a Traktorgyár', (1971), by the Vörös Csillag Traktorgyár, now RÁBA Kispesti Öntöde-Es Gépgyar KFT., pp. 15, 17.

2. Report of the Tariff Commission, Volume 4. 1909. The Engineering Industries: paragraphs 896 (Witness No. 256, Frederick Andrew, Robey and Co. Ltd.), and 1037 (Firm No. 884).

3. Ibid., paragraph 683 (Witness No. 270, identified as Marshall, Sons and Co. Ltd.).

4. Ibid., paragraphs 699 (Witness No. 270), 987 (Firm No. 884), 988 (Firm No. 1303).

5. 2nd Report of the Royal Commission on Depression of Trade and Industry, 1886, Part 2, Appendix E, p. 107.
The Lincolnshire Chronicle, 23rd March, 1935: article on William Foster and Co. Ltd., based on information from Sir William Tritton.

6. 2nd Report of the Royal Commission on Depression of Trade and Industry, 1886, Part 2, Appendix E, pp. 106-107.

7. Report of the Tariff Commission, Volume 4, 1909, The Engineering Industries: paragraphs 559 and 560 (Witness No. 257, A. Bornemann, Ruston Proctor).

8. *The Lincolnshire Chronicle*, 6th December, 1952.

9. 2nd Report of the Royal Commission on Depression of Trade and Industry, 1886, Part 2, Appendix E, p. 107.

10. *The Engineer*, 27th March, 1908, p. 313; April 10th 1908, pp. 365-366.

11. Report of the Tariff Commission, Volume 4, 1909, The Engineering Industries: Paragraphs 548 (Witness No. 256, Frederick Andrew, Robey and Co. Ltd.), 684 (Witness No. 270), 925, 987 (Firm No. 884).

12. '70 Éves a Traktorgyár', (1971), by the Vörös Csillag Traktorgyár, now RÁBA Kispesti Öntöde-Es Gépgyar KFT., pp. 17, 32.

13. *The Implement and Machinery Review*, 1st May, 1920, pp. 108-109.

14. Report of the Tariff Commission, Volume 4, 1909, The Engineering Industries: paragraph 548 (Witness No. 256, Frederick Andrew, Robey and Co. Ltd.).

15. Ibid., paragraphs 925, 987 (Firm No. 884).

16. Ibid., paragraph 675 (Witness No. 269, J. E. Ransome, Ransomes, Sims, and Jefferies Ltd.).

Chapter II Developments in the export trade

1. *Power on the land*, A Centenary History of the Agricultural Engineers Association 1875-1975, by Robert Trow-Smith, pp. 39, 43.

2. Report of the Tariff Commission, Volume 4, 1909, The Engineering Industries: section VI. – statistical tables, table 30, paragraph 1300.

3. *Journal of the Road Locomotive Society*, December 1964, p. 4, Address by H. L. Drewitt, O.B.E.

4. *The Implement and Machinery Review*, 1st October, 1909, p. 714.

5. Ibid., 1st August, 1912, p. 493.

6. Ibid., 1st April, 1904, p. 1333; 2nd May, 1907, p. 63.

7. Ibid., 1st December, 1910, pp. 988-989; 1st February, 1913, p. 1325; 1st May, 1924, p. 67.

8. Ibid., 2nd May, 1907, p. 62; 1st December, 1910, p. 988.

9. *Journal of The Royal Agricultural Society of England*, Volume 52, 1892, p. 253, 'The Evolution of Agricultural Implements' by Dan Pidgeon.

10. *The Implement and Machinery Review*, 2nd September, 1903, p. 531.

11. Ibid., 1st December, 1910, p. 988.

12. *The Lincolnshire Magazine*, Volume 2, parts 1-12, September 1934 to July 1936: 'The origin of the thrashing machine' by Sir William Tritton, J.P., p. 59.

Chapter III Company matters and the human side of business

1. *The Lincolnshire Magazine*, Volume 2, parts 1-12, September 1934 to July 1936: 'The origin of the thrashing machine' by Sir William Tritton, J.P., p. 59.

2. *The Lincolnshire Chronicle*, January 1945, article 'A Lincoln Industrial Tragedy' by "W. M.".

3. *The Implement and Machinery Review*, 1st August, 1920, pp. 569-570.

4. *The Engineer*, 23rd May, 1913, article 'A visit to a Lincoln Engineering Works', p. 552.
   Walter Haynes' unpublished 'History of Ruston and Hornsby Limited', Volume 2, pp. 81-83.

5. *The Lincolnshire Chronicle*, January 1945, article 'A Lincoln Industrial Tragedy' by 'W.M.'.

6. *The Engineer*, 22nd May, 1942, obituary of H. F. L. Orcutt, p. 430.

7. *The Implement and Machinery Review*, 3rd February, 1902, p. 1064.

8. *The Engineer*, 17th January, 1908, article 'The training of engineering apprentices', pp. 52-54
   The Implement and Machinery Review, 1st March, 1907, pp. 1321-1322.

9. Walter Haynes' unpublished 'History of Ruston and Hornsby Limited', Volume 2, p. 97.

Chapter IV **Sales**

1. *Harvests of Change*, The Royal Agricultural Society of England 1838-1988, by Nicholas Goddard, pp. 55, 57.

2. The Royal Agricultural Society of England – catalogue for the Seventieth Annual Exhibition held at Gloucester, 22nd-26th June, 1909: pp. 50, 73-74, 143, 148-152, 158, 167-168.

3. *Journal of The Royal Agricultural Society of England*, Volume 16, 1855.

4. *The Implement and Machinery Review*, 1st August 1918, pp. 413-414.

5. Ibid., 1st December, 1933, p. 665.

6. *Lincolnshire Life*, January 1964, 'Was exporting ever fun?' – article by J. R. Marshall, pp. 54-55.

7. 2nd Report of the Royal Commission on Depression of Trade and Industry, 1886, Part 2, Appendix E, p. 107.

8. *One Hundred Years of Good Company* by Bernard Newman. Published by Ruston and Hornsby Limited in 1957 on the occasion of their centenary, p. 42.

9. General note: history of Agar Cross researched from private documents in the possession of Avdel plc.

Chapter V George Thurlow and Sons Limited

1. This paragraph is compiled from the following sources researched by the Suffolk Record Office, Ipswich:
    1871 Census, Stowmarket: Ref. RG 10/1734, folio 67, pp. 9-10.
    1881 Census, Stowmarket: Ref. RG 11/1851, folio 47, pp. 13.
    Kelly's Trades Directories, Suffolk: 1875, 1879, 1883, 1885, 1888.
    Ipswich Journal, 1st November, 1890.
2. *Stowmarket Weekly Post*, 19th April, 1906.
3. General note: history of George Thurlow and Sons Limited researched from private documents in the possession of Mr. J. Thurlow.

Chapter VI The late George Cox and Ruston's

1. Walter Haynes' unpublished 'History of Ruston and Hornsby Limited', Volume 1, pp. 92-93, Volume 2, p. 1.
2. *Engineering* Magazine, 2nd July, 1920, article on 'The Works of Messrs. Ruston and Hornsby Ltd., Lincoln', p. 7.

Chapter VII Contracting

1. *The Implement and Machinery Review*, 1st August, 1930, pp. 405-406.
2. Ibid.

Chapter VIII The late Henry Marshall

1. *Britannia News*, The Works Journal of Marshall Sons and Company Ltd., May 1959, article by Henry Marshall.

Chapter IX Observations, 1914-1990

1. *The Implement and Machinery Review*, 1st July, 1915, p. 355.
2. Ibid, 1st May, 1934, p. 57.
3. Committee on Industry and Trade – Survey of Metal Industries, part 4, H.M.S.O., 1928, p. 160.

4. *The Implement and Machinery Review*, 1st April, 1921, pp. 1852-1854 and 1st October, 1921, p. 821.

5. Ibid.

6. Ibid., 1st August, 1930, pp. 405-406.

7. Ibid., 1st June, 1920, pp. 254-255.

8. Ibid., 1st July, 1934, p. 236.

9. Ibid., 1st April, 1935, p. 1077.

Appendix A

GEORGE THURLOW AND SONS LIMITED

1. Traction engine sales: new engines sold between 1903 and 1935 (including limited sales of steam tractors, ploughing engines and steam rollers).

Sales by manufacturer:

Marshall	146
Burrell	55
Garrett	54
Clayton and Shuttleworth	41
Ruston Proctor / Ruston and Hornsby	32
Fowler	20
Foden	7
Wallis and Steevens	5
Mclaren	2
Robey	2
Allchin	1
Foster	1
Ransomes Sims and Jefferies	1
Tasker	1
	368

Annual sales:

Year		Year		Year	
1903	21	1915	21	1927	2
1904	16	1916	9	1928	4
1905	19	1917	8	1929	1
1906	21	1918	7	1930	nil
1907	21	1919	22	1931	nil
1908	17	1920	22	1932	2
1909	22	1921	3	1933	nil
1910	29	1922	5	1934	nil
1911	33	1923	3	1935	1
1912	20	1924	1		368
1913	18	1925	5		
1914	13	1926	2		

2. Portable engine sales: new engines sold between 1903 and 1919:

Sales by manufacturer:

Marshall	22
Garrett	4
Ruston Proctor / Ruston and Hornsby	3
Clayton and Shuttleworth	1
	30

Annual sales:

1903	3	1909	3	1915	1
1904	2	1910	3	1916	3
1905	1	1911	3	1917	nil
1906	2	1912	3	1918	nil
1907	2	1913	nil	1919	1
1908	2	1914	1		30

3. Thrashing machine sales: new machines sold between 1903 and 1955:

Sales by manufacturer:

Marshall	508
Clayton and Shuttleworth	106
Foster	71
Ransomes Sims and Jefferies	71
Ruston Proctor / Ruston and Hornsby	53
Garrett	46
Tasker	8
Burrell	2
	865

Annual sales:

1903	19	1922	14	1941	42
1904	13	1923	14	1942	26
1905	23	1924	14	1943	26
1906	20	1925	6	1944	48
1907	38	1926	4	1945	13
1908	28	1927	6	1946	33
1909	26	1928	7	1947	28
1910	29	1929	7	1948	31
1911	26	1930	6	1949	21
1912	28	1931	1	1950	15
1913	19	1932	3	1951	10
1914	19	1933	4	1952	7
1915	7	1934	1	1953	6
1916	9	1935	17	1954	6
1917	16	1936	18	1955	2
1918	4	1937	13		865
1919	12	1938	10		
1920	22	1939	11		
1921	16	1940	21		

Appendix B

TRACTION ENGINES OWNED BY JOSEPH GRIFFIN, BRUERN GRANGE, OXFORDSHIRE

Description	Number	Built	Acquired	Name
Ransomes, Sims & Jefferies compound steam tractor – 4 n.h.p.	26813	1915	1916	'Mary'
Fowler single cylinder agricultural engine – 6 n.h.p.	Not known	Not known	1918	'Old John'
Fowler compound ploughing engine, class K7 – 12 n.h.p.	15270	1919	1919	'Crystobel'
Fowler compound ploughing engine, class K7 – 12 n.h.p.	15271	1919	1919	'Sylvia'
Fowler single cylinder agricultural engine class A4 – 8 n.h.p.	7914	1897	1924-5	'Frank Reading'
Wantage single cylinder agricultural engine – 8 n.h.p.	1522	1905	1926	Un-named
Ransomes, Sims & Jefferies compound steam tractor – 4 n.h.p.	39088	1928	1928	'Countess of Nottingham'
Aveling & Porter single cylinder agricultural engine – 6 n.h.p.	5086	1902	1936	Un-named
R. J. and H. Wilder ploughing engine – a Fowler single cylinder ploughing engine, rebuilt by Wilder's and incorporating an 'Allen' single cylinder – 12 n.h.p., piston-valve.	Not known	Not known	1938	Un-named

This list is based on information kindly supplied by Bob Griffin and the late Alan Duke, former Engine Records Officer of the Road Locomotive Society.

A Savage traction engine traversing the Cambridgeshire floods of 1912.

Bibliography

Britannia News – Marshall, Sons and Company Limited.
The Compleat Traction Engineman – E. E. Kimbell, 1973.
East Anglian Traction Engine Club, *Steam Preservation Quarterly.*
The Engineer.
Engineering magazine.
Farm Tools Implements and Machines in Britain – R. Morgan, 1984.
Harvests of Change – N. Goddard, 1988.
A History of Modern Hungary 1867-1986 – K. Hoensch, 1988.
A History of Ruston and Hornsby (unpublished) – W. Haynes.
The Implement and Machinery Review.
The Ipswich Journal.
Kelly's Trade Directories, Suffolk: 1875, 1879, 1883, 1885, 1888.
The Lincolnshire Chronicle.
Lincolnshire Engines Worldwide – R. Brooks, 1988.
Lincolnshire Life.
The Lincolnshire Magazine.
The Machinery Market.
Manufacturers' and Agents' literature.
National Traction Engine Trust, *Steaming.*
One Hundred Years of Good Company – B. Newman, 1957.
Power on the Land – R. Trow-Smith, 1977.
Private documents in the possession of Avdel plc.
Private documents in the possession of Oxfordshire Museums Store.
Private documents in the possession of the Thurlow family.
Report of the Tariff Commission, Volume 4, 1909, The Engineering Industries.
The Road Locomotive Society, Journal.
The Royal Agricultural Society of England, Catalogue for 1909 Annual Show at Gloucester.
The Royal Agricultural Society of England, Journal.
Royal Commission on Depression of Trade and Industry – 1st and 2nd Reports, 1885 and 1886.
70 Éves a Traktorgyár – Vörös Csillag Traktorgyár, 1971: Now RÁBA Kispesti, Öntöde-Es Gépgyár KFT.

A Souvenir of the Royal Show, Lincoln, 1907 – Harrison, Photographer, and J. W. Ruddock & Sons, Printers, Lincoln.

Steam Thrashing in the Cotswolds – M. B. Thexton, 1986.

Stowmarket Census, 1871, 1881.

Stowmarket Mercury.

Stowmarket Weekly Post.

Survey of Metal Industries – Part 4, Committee on Industry and Trade, 1930.

The Traction Engine – F. H. Gillford, 1952.

Waterloo Iron Works – L. T. C. Rolt, 1969.

Index